Hemp Foods & Oils
for Health

*Your Guide to Cooking,
Nutrition, and Body Care*

Gero Leson · Petra Pless
with John W. Roulac

The Industrial Hemp Information Network

Sebastopol, California

Publisher: HEMPTECH
Authors: Gero Leson and Petra Pless, with John W. Roulac
Editor: Sonia Nordenson
Cover Design: Catherine A. Greco
Cover Photo: Kim Stephenson
Layout: White Light Publishing
Printing: Vaughn Printing

First Printing June 1999

ISBN 1-886874-05-0

The cover of this book is printed on Vanguard Hemp—25% hemp, 75% post-consumer content from Living Tree Paper Company. The hemp was pulped utilizing a chlorine-free process. Visit www.livingtreepaper.com or call 800-309-2974. The interior text is printed on recycled-content paper.

Acknowledgments to Christel Dillbohner, Janet Crolius-Jacob, and Wendy Millstine for turning the recipes into tasty reality, and to nova-Institute in Hürth, Germany, for initiating, coordinating, and reviewing some of the research.

Special thanks to all reviewers of the manuscript:

Kelly Fitzpatrick of Saskatchewan Nutraceutical Network; Paul Gaylon of Herbal Products & Development; Dr. Franjo Grotenhermen of nova-Institute; Michael Holcomb of Historical Harvests; Jean Laprise of Kenex, Ltd.; Dr. Helga Mölleken of Bergische Unversität Wuppertal; Dr. Roman Przybylski of the University of Manitoba Department of Foods and Nutrition; Kelly Smith of Hempola; Don Wirtshafter of The Ohio Hempery.

Credit for data and suggestions, including information not referenced in the bibliography, goes to: La Chanvrière de l'Aube, Kenex, Ltd., nova-Institut, Helga Mölleken, Richard Rose (Hempnut, Inc.), Kelly Smith, Don Wirtshafter and Heather Wakefield.

❧❧ HEMPTECH
The Industrial Hemp Information Network

P. O. Box 1716, Sebastopol, CA 95473, USA
Tel: (707) 823-2800, Fax: (707) 823-2424
Email: info@hemptech.com
Web sites: www.hemptech.com and www.hemp-foods.com

HEMPTECH is a print and Internet publishing firm offering hemp books, reports, and videos. Our Web site offers an online hemp news service and a hemp products directory featuring more than 600 companies.

CONTENTS

A Hempseed Primer

What's healthful about hempseeds and hemp oil?

Hempseeds are a rich source of essential amino and fatty acids. These vital nutrients cannot be manufactured by the human body and must be present in our diet. About 75 percent of the fatty acids in hemp oil consist of a balanced ratio of the two essential fatty acids including omega-3 alpha-linolenic acid, usually underrepresented in our diet. Further, the seed-meat protein contains all essential amino acids in a well-balanced ratio, mostly in easily digestible form. This makes hemp a strong rival to soy as a protein source. Finally, hempseeds contain other essential nutrients, such as the antioxidant vitamin E, minerals, and lecithin.

Can I cook with hempseeds and hemp oil?

Yes. The hulled seeds can replace soy, nuts, and grains in many products, from breads, pastries, and snacks to sauces, dressings, and non-dairy products. Hemp oil can also replace other cold-pressed oils in salads, in warm dishes, on bread, and for light sautéing. It is not recommended for frying and deep-frying because of its high content of delicate unsaturated fatty acids.

What makes hemp oil an excellent choice for body-care products?

Its high content of polyunsaturated fatty acids makes hemp oil an ideal emollient and moisturizer in skin-care products such as facial creams and body lotions. By soothing and restoring dry skin, body-care products containing hemp oil can reduce skin discomfort and heal minor abrasions. In hair-care products, hemp oil can impart gloss and manageability to hair and bring relief from dry scalp.

Why is hemp good for our environment?

To date, hemp farmers in Canada and Europe have not needed to use herbicides or pesticides. Hemp suppresses weeds and also improves the soil for subsequent crops in rotation. For these reasons, it is particularly well suited for use in organic and sustainable farming. The bast fiber and seeds produced by the hemp plant provide raw materials for thousands of useful products. Hemp is a valuable renewable resource that can reduce our overreliance on cotton, soybeans, timber, and petroleum.

Can hemp foods get me high?

No. Small amounts of THC, the psychoactive ingredient in marijuana, can stick to the outer hulls of seeds from industrial hemp, and may thus be found in hemp oil and other hempseed products. Yet THC concentrations in properly cleaned seeds from the low THC varieties used for North American food products are much too low to cause any narcotic effects. Products from hulled seeds contain even lower levels of THC-less than 2 ppm (equal to 0.0002 percent). Smoking industrial hemp would only give the smoker a headache.

Can eating hemp foods cause a positive drug test?

In a few cases, the consumption of hemp oil and other hempseed products has resulted in a positive urine test for marijuana. Generally, ingesting hemp oil or hemp foods will not cause a positive test result, and using hulled hempseeds will dramatically reduce any chance of testing positive. Canadian and European hemp-food producers are aware of the issue, and consider it in their quality-control process. The inefficient transfer of THC via the skin prevents positive tests from the use of skin-care products containing hemp oil.

Foreword

Seeds are important foods for human health, and hempseeds contain a unique combination of beneficial ingredients. Hempseeds are rich in dietary fiber and in the essential fatty acids that are lacking in the usual North American diet: alpha- and gamma-linolenic acid (GLA). Essential fatty acids (EFAs) are components of fat that our bodies need to be healthy, but that we cannot make ourselves.

EFAs come in two families, called omega-3 and omega-6. Our diets have been systematically depleted of omega-3 EFAs by modern farming and food processing methods. Alpha-linolenic acid is the leading omega-3 EFA in the human diet, and hemp oil is one of the few seed oils containing significant quantities of this vital fatty acid. Although omega-6 EFAs are frequently added to foods through the use of common vegetable oils like corn, sunflower, and safflower, many people are unable to properly utilize omega-6 oils because the enzymes needed to metabolize these oils are hampered by hormonal problems, genetic weaknesses, environmental toxicity, the effects of aging, or complex nutritional imbalances. For these people, GLA is an indispensable nutrient; it allows their bodies to bypass the usual enzymatic blocks to omega-6 utilization.

In my work with patients, in my teaching of other doctors, and in my writing, I consistently emphasize the importance of establishing a properly balanced intake of omega-3 and omega-6 EFAs. I provide my patients and my readers with a series of questions they can answer to see if they need an "oil change." For many people suffering from problems as varied as fatigue, allergies, arthritis (or just aches and pains), dry skin, premenstrual syndrome, and severe menstrual cramps, or for those who are interested in achieving and maintaining a high level of wellness, the right EFA balance is a key step. The availability of hemp oil, with its special mixture of Alpha-linolenic acid and GLA, will make the journey to health much smoother for many people. Fortunately, hempseeds and their oil have a delicious nutty flavor that makes them an appealing food, not just good medicine.

— Leo Galland, M.D.
Author of *Power Healing*
(Random House, 1998)
and Director of the Foundation for
Integrated Medicine in New York, NY
www.mdheal.org

1

The Revival of an Ancient Crop

Hemp, a plant traditionally used for fiber, food, and body care and then nearly forgotten, is making a strong comeback. Besides the numerous modern uses of the fiber, whole and hulled hempseeds are used for snacks and baked goods, and the oil from hempseeds is stocked in the cold storage of natural-food stores and found on the ingredient list of natural cosmetics.

The rediscovery of hemp oil has been made especially visible by advertising campaigns for body-care products that contain it, run by such companies as The Body Shop and Alterna. However, the real pioneering work has been done by the many American and European firms that have developed and promoted hempseeds and hemp oil products since the early 1990s.

The Case for Hempseeds
What is driving this comeback? Here are six key factors:

1. Hempseeds contain high amounts of several nutrients the body can't do without. More than 75 percent of the oil consists of essential fatty acids, indispensable for cell growth, healthy skin, and disease prevention. Hempseeds also provide all of the essential amino acids needed to build muscle tissue, enzymes, membranes, or antibodies. Thus, hempseeds qualify as a valuable nutritional "package deal."
2. Hulled hempseeds combine the versatility and nutritional value of nuts and soybeans. They are tasty, and can be used in everything from snacks, spreads, dips, and sauces to non-dairy milk, cheeses, and ice creams.
3. Properly produced hemp oil has a delicate, nutty flavor, and is finding its place as a staple food in the modern gourmet kitchen.
4. Hemp oil used in body-care products protects the skin by reducing dryness, helps alleviate skin-disease problems, and may slow the skin's aging process.
5. Hemp oil contains high amounts of several polyunsaturated fatty acids (PUFAs) that have therapeutic effects in the treatment of various

Hemp can be used . . .

diseases including atopic eczema, psoriasis, acne, arthritis, multiple sclerosis, cancer, PMS and menopausal moodswings, as well as in the prevention of cardiovascular diseases, osteoporosis, and cancer.

6. Hemp is an eco-friendly crop that almost never needs pesticides, so consumers needn't worry about pesticide residues in their products or the environment.

Hempseed products chart

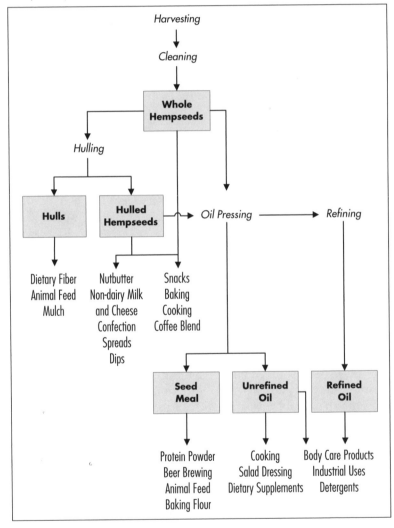

A Brief History of Hemp

Hemp (botanical name *Cannabis sativa*) is one of our oldest and most versatile plants. Documentation of its use dates back as far as the 28th century B.C., and it likely had been used long before that. Ancient China domesticated hemp from a wild plant, developing breeding, farming, and processing techniques. The fiber was used for textiles and the seeds were used for food. In Europe, hemp fiber was used in rope and fabrics at least as early as 800 B.C. and was reported to make fine cloth by the Greek historian Herodotus around 450 B.C. In the following centuries, the seeds and flowers were named as a cure for numerous diseases: as an analgesic; for sores and skin diseases; and for coughs, jaundice, and colic. At the same time, hemp had become an indispensable source of fiber for ropes and coarse textiles. When the art of papermaking arrived in Europe from China in the 14th century, rags of hemp and flax became the sole materials used for paper. Its wet strength made hemp fiber the natural choice for England and Spain when rigging ships during their conquest of the globe.

The American colonists also relied heavily on hemp; in the 1600s, colonial governments even mandated settlers to grow the crop. George Washington and Thomas Jefferson farmed hemp, and the first drafts of the Declaration of Independence were written on hemp paper.

Yet the tall, strong hemp plants were never an easy crop to harvest and process. Before the outer bast fibers can be further processed, they need to be separated from the woody core of the stalks, the so-called hurds —a labor-intensive procedure. In the 18th century, more convenient and economical resources appeared: cotton displaced hemp, flax, and wool from the textile market, we learned how to make pulp and paper from wood, and inexpensive imported fibers—sisal, jute, and abaca—became available. Hempseeds, a by-product of the fiber, fell into oblivion along with the stalks. By the early 20th century, hemp had become a niche crop in most industrialized countries. The existence of its botanical relative marijuana—Cannabis varieties containing psychoactive substances— didn't help hemp's status. In the late 1930s, in many Western countries,

From a 1765 letter:

"I am prepared to deliver...hemp in your port, watered and prepared according to the Act of Parliament."

— George Washington

potential   products!

marijuana prohibition tied hemp cultivation in bureaucratic red tape. During World War II, the United States and Germany revived hemp farming when they lost some of their overseas fiber supplies. Yet, after 1945, the use of hemp and other natural fibers waned while the use of synthetic fibers rapidly expanded. Only in Eastern Europe, China, and a few other Asian countries did the labor-intensive production of hemp continue. While most Western countries had outlawed hemp, France continued to grow it for specialty pulp production. French farmers were even subsidized by the European Union, to support the farming of domestic fiber crops. Yet, by the 1970s, in contrast to its former importance, *Cannabis sativa* should have been listed as an endangered species. [1, 9, 14, 16] *

The Rediscovery of Hemp

Then, in the late 1980s and early 1990s, hemp was rediscovered in the West. Several books portraying it as *the* versatile and environmentally friendly crop created new demand for hemp textiles and body-care products. Cottage industries for manufacturing and distribution began to spring up. No doubt, the "smokeability" of some Cannabis varieties added an element of excitement and mystique to industrial hemp that is largely missing with other crops. At the same time, farmers in some European countries who were looking for new crops—and motivated by novelty and subsidy—were successful in relegalizing hemp. Since then, hemp acreage has continued to grow, providing raw materials to gradually expanding markets for fiber and seeds. Since 1998, hemp is also farmed commercially in Canada, and the first North American-grown hempseeds are now available to the expanding food market.

To date, twenty-nine countries allow farmers to grow industrial hemp. In the United States, irrational debate over the threat that hemp farming may pose to our youth has so far kept the crop illegal.

The oft-expressed concern that hemp farming may aid the production and use of marijuana is unsubstantiated. For one thing, hemp's commercial varieties have been bred to contain very low levels of the psychoactive ingredient THC, short for delta-9-tetrahydrocannabinol. The low THC content makes futile any effort to get high from smoking industrial hemp. Only varieties containing less than 0.3 percent THC in their flower portions can legally be farmed in Canada and the European Union, while marijuana flowers typically contain 3 to 20 percent. Also, industrial hemp is grown differently from marijuana, so industrial hemp farming does not provide a good camouflage for marijuana cultivation.

---

* *see Bibliography*

The   following   list   .   .   .

The various myths around industrial hemp and marijuana have been comprehensively refuted (see Chapter Seven). [1,17]

Iowa farmers in the 1940s bundling hemp fibers utilizing specialized harvesting equipment.

Hemp, a Modern Crop

Hemp is a fast-growing, versatile plant. Its core, fibers, seeds, and flowers can serve as raw material for numerous products: food, paper, textiles, carpets, insulation materials, fiber-reinforced plastics, animal bedding, body-care products, aromatic essential oils, and many others. These products often have technical advantages over competing products, are cost-competitive, and provide environmental benefits.

In particular, hemp requires no herbicide use, since it outgrows, shades, and thereby suppresses weeds. Pests such as insects or fungi rarely cause significant losses, thus generally eliminating pesticide use. Hemp also improves the soil and clears it of weeds, controls certain root diseases, and often improves the yields of subsequent crops. As Dr. Iván

.   .   .   *highlights   particular*

Bócsa and Michael Karus explain in *The Cultivation of Hemp*[1], it's a cooperative crop, useful in rotation with other plants. Hemp is not a miracle plant, yet, in the years to come it will make an important contribution to a more sustainable economy.

An observer of the debate over industrial hemp in the U.S. may feel that the phrase "the land of the free and the home of the brave" has become a forgotten relic. Perhaps the reintroduction of industrial hemp into the economy could be an element on our path to a more just and sustainable society.

A John Deere Kemper harvester cuts and chops hemp stalks in a HempFlax field in Holland.

h e m p s e e d   p r o d u c t s :

2

What's in a Hempseed?

When talking about hemp foods and hemp body-care products, we mean products made from hempseeds. Botanically, the seeds are tiny nuts that develop on the female flowers of the hemp plants. When they mature in late summer, they develop a thin, crunchy hull, gray or brownish in color with a marbled pattern. The seeds are small: 1,000 of them weigh, depending on the variety, 0.5 to 0.9 ounces (15 to 25 grams). For comparison, 1,000 hulled peanuts weigh about 18 to 25 ounces (500 to 700 grams).

The 1895 *Yearbook of the United States Department of Agriculture* stated:

"The nut-like fruits, commonly called seeds, are used in great quantities in bird food. They are nearly egg-shaped in outline, flattened at the margins. Color, dark gray, with fine, net-like, whitish markings on the smooth and shiny surface. The seeds . . . are filled with a whitish embryo which yields 30 to 35 percent of a peculiar-smelling, mild-tasting oil, greenish yellow when freshly pressed, becoming brownish yellow with age. Hempseed oil is used to a considerable extent in the preparation of paints and varnishes . . . In Europe it enters largely into the composition of soft soaps . . . Hemp will thrive in most parts of the United States . . . The value of hemp for fiber, birdseed, and oil would seem to make its cultivation a very profitable one."

Hemp seeds

Vertical cut through a hempseed

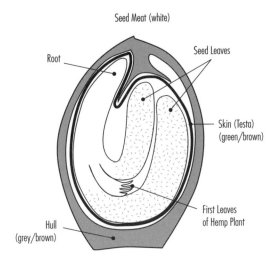

Seed Meat (white)

Root

Seed Leaves

Skin (Testa)
(green/brown)

First Leaves
of Hemp Plant

Hull
(grey/brown)

Redrawn with permission from Robert Clarke.

The seed hull protects the embryo, which consists of two pale seed leaves (the "meat" of the seed) and a tiny root. The hull contains mainly dietary fiber-carbohydrates that we can eat but not digest-and chlorophyll, which gives hemp oil its green color.

The meat represents the seed's "power bar" for energy storage and building materials. Proteins, small amounts of carbohydrates, and fat stored in tiny oil droplets in the cells make up most of the meat. Additional ingredients are found in smaller quantities: vitamins, lecithin, phospholipids, phytosterols, and others. [1, 9, 14]

Compared to other nuts, hempseeds have a few points in their favor:

- Hemp oil typically contains 75 percent essential fatty acids, including 15 to 20 percent alpha-linolenic acid, an omega-3 fatty acid often deficient in our diet. The oil contains only about 10 percent

Hulled Hempseed

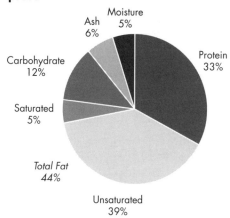

Whole Hempseed

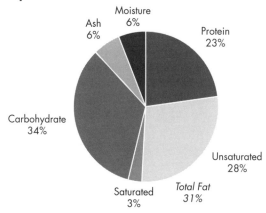

Source: adapted from Jones 1995, nova 1998, Kenex Ltd., HempNut, Inc.

of the less desirable saturated fatty acids. It also contains small amounts of two other polyunsaturated fatty acids that we may be short on, i.e gamma-linolenic and stearidonic acid.

- The seed protein contains all the essential amino acids in a favorable ratio, and mostly in an easily digestible form.
- Their flavor makes the seeds as tasty as they are nutritious.

• B i s c o t t i • B o d y l o t i o n s •

	Whole Hempseeds	Hulled Hempseeds
Nutritional analyses		
Energy	500 kCal/100g	560 kCal/100g
Protein	23 g/100g	33 g/100g
Total fat	31 g/100g	44 g/100g
Saturated	3 g/100g	5 g/100g
Unsaturated	28 g/100g	39 g/100g
Carbohydrates	34 g/100g	12 g/100g
Dietary fiber	33 g/100g	5 g/100g
Sugars	1 g/100g	2 g/100g
Ash	6 g/100g	6 g/100g
Moisture	6 g/100g	5 g/100g
Minerals		
Calcium	70–180 mg/100g	
Iron	5–20 mg/100g	
Sodium	2–10 mg/100g	
THC content	10–30 ppm	<2 ppm

Notes: data on vitamin content are limited and inconclusive and were not included

    1 ppm = 1 mg/kg

Source: adapted from nova-Institute 1998, Kenex Ltd., HempNut, Inc. Wirtshafter in Bioresource Hemp 1995

Typical specifications for whole and hulled hempseeds

•   *B e v e r a g e s*   •   *B i r d s e e d*   •

	Hemp Oil
Fatty Acid Analysis	
Saturated fatty acids	in % of total fatty acids
Palmitic acid (16:0)	6–9%
Stearic acid (18:0)	2–3.5%
Arachidic acid (20:0)	1–3%
Behenic acid (22:0)	<0.3%
Total saturated fatty acids	9–11%
Unsaturated Fatty Acids	in % of total fatty acids
Oleic acid (18:1 omega-9)	8.5–16%
Linoleic acid (18:2 omega-6)	53–60%
gamma-Linolenic acid GLA (18:3 omega-6)	1–4%
alpha-Linolenic acid (18:3 omega-3)	15–25%
Stearidonic acid (18:4 omega-3)	0.4–2%
Eicosaenoic acid (20:1)	<0.5%
Total unsaturated fatty acids	89–91%

Chemical Analyses

Vitamin E	100–150 mg/100g (mostly gamma-tocopherol)
	13–20 IU/100g (as alpha-tocopherol equivalents)
Chlorophyll	50–20 ppm
THC content	2–20 ppm
Specific gravity	0.92 kg/l
Iodine value	155–170
Peroxide Value	4–7 meq O_2/kg
Free Fatty Acids	1.5–2.0% as Oleic Acid
Phosphatides	100–400 ppm
Smoke Point	330 ° F (165 °C)
Melting Point	18 °F (-8 °C)

Notes: typical ranges for Central and Northern European varieties
  1 ppm = 1 mg/kg

Source: adapted from La Chanvrière de l'Aube, Deferne & Pate 1996, nova-Institute 1998,
Przybylski in Bioresource Hemp 1997, Wirtshafter in Bioresource Hemp 1995

Typical specifications for unrefined hemp oil

• *B r e a d* • *B r e a d i n g* •

3

Hemp Oil: Filled With Essential Nutrients

Hemp oil has been the most visible of all hempseed products to date. The following review will provide a better understanding of its potential benefits.

Fats and oils are very similar in their chemical composition. They are built from fatty acids, one of nature's fundamental building units. Their high energy content makes them a valuable food and storage medium. Fatty acids are also needed for the construction of cell walls, for the protective outer layer of our skin, and for the production of hormones, prostaglandins, and other compounds that serve as messengers and control systems.

Nature produces fatty acids in different sizes and shapes, varying their physical properties and nutritional value. Most important is the distinction between saturated and unsaturated fatty acids. The debate over "good and bad" fats and their impact on cardiovascular health actually centers around this distinction. Two particularly important unsaturated fatty acids are the essential fatty acids (EFAs) omega-6 linoleic acid and omega-3 alpha-linolenic acid, which the body cannot synthesize from other molecules. They must be present in our diet in sufficiently large quantities or we will develop symptoms of deficiency and, eventually, serious illness.[5] Much of hemp oil's nutritional appeal is that it provides both EFAs in a ratio beneficial for humans. For those interested in the nature of fatty acids and their use by the body, the following section can serve as an overview and reference.

Fatty Acids: Properties and Metabolism

By definition, fats—primarily from mammals—are solid at room temperature, while oils—primarily from fish and plant seeds—are liquid. Both consist to more than 90 percent of so-called triglycerides. These molecules are built from a glycerol backbone to which three fatty acids are attached with "ester bonds." The three fatty acids on a triglyceride can be all the same or all different types. The size and shape of the fatty acids determine the physical and chemical properties of an oil and its nutritional value.

B r e a k f a s t   c e r e a l   •   B r o w n i e s   •

Chemical structure of alpha-linolenic acid in a triglyceride

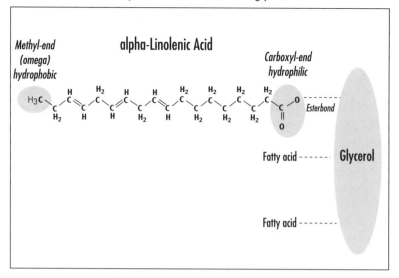

Fatty acids are chains of varying length, made of carbon (C-) atoms and enveloped by a hull of hydrogen (H-) atoms. The "omega" or "methyl" end of the chain is hydrophobic—it dislikes water. A carboxylic acid group (-COOH) renders the other end "water-liking." In natural fats and oils, the chain length of fatty acids may vary from 4 to 28 C-atoms. Most common in vegetable oils are chain lengths of 16 to 20. There are two distinct groups of fatty acids.

In *saturated fatty acids*, every C-atom is bound to its neighboring c-atom by stable, "saturated" bonds. The triglycerides composed of saturated fatty acids align well. These triglycerides are more "sticky" and solid at room temperature, i.e., typical fats. The body uses saturated fatty acids shorter than 12 C-atoms mostly for rapid energy production.

Because saturated bonds are also more resistant to oxidation, they are less prone to turning rancid (see Chapter Five). Major sources of saturated fatty acids are animal fats (butter, lard, beef tallow), coconut, and palm kernel fats and oils. Because of their stability and low cost they have traditionally been used for frying. Unfortunately, they also increase blood levels of LDL (low density lipoprotein or "bad") cholesterol, a sticky substance that helps form arterial plaque (blood-vessel deposits that impede blood flow and increase the risk of heart attacks and strokes).

Unsaturated fatty acids feature at least one unsaturated, or double, bond between C-atoms. Unsaturated fatty acids are specified by their number of C-atoms and double bonds, and by the location of the first double bond in the chain. For example, alpha-linolenic acid has 18 C-atoms and three double bonds. The first one is located on the 3rd C-atom, counting from the omega end. Thus, its shorthand formula is (18:3 omega-3). Unsaturated bonds cause fatty acids to bend. This increases the flexibility and reduces the stickiness of these fatty acids and their triglycerides. Unsaturated fatty acids also react more easily with oxygen, free radicals, and other organic compounds. While it suits technical applications, such as in paint, and provides health benefits, this instability also makes oils high in polyunsaturated fatty acids (PUFAs) less stable. Several PUFAs have important functions in the human body.

Essential fatty acids: Particularly important for human nutrition are the two essential fatty acids (EFAs) linoleic acid (18:2 omega-6) and alpha-linolenic acid (18:3 omega-3). These cannot be synthesized by the body and must be present in our diet. Most oil seeds contain high concentrations of linoleic acid, but substantial amounts of alpha-linolenic acid are found in the oils of only a few common seeds and nuts: flax (typically 58 percent), hemp (15 to 20 percent), canola (13 percent), and soybean (7 percent). The fats of fish and mammals contain only little alpha-linolenic acid.

Omega families: The two EFAs themselves do not have specific physiological functions but are converted by enzymes to longer and more unsaturated fatty acids (see figure). In humans, the metabolites of either EFA maintain the location of the first double bond, thus keeping their "omega-3" or "omega-6" rating, respectively. The longer chain PUFAs are further converted into several series of prostaglandins, hormone-like substances that regulate many cell functions. These prostaglandins control, often in competition with each other, the progress of inflammations, fever, and pain. They increase or reduce blood pressure and affect the coagulation of thrombocytes. Since the same enzymes are used in the metabolism of both EFAs, an excess of members of one omega-family can reduce activity in the other, thus shifting the balance in some of the functions controlled by fatty acids and prostaglandins.

Candies • Caramels • Caramel

Metabolic pathways from essential fatty acids to prostaglandins

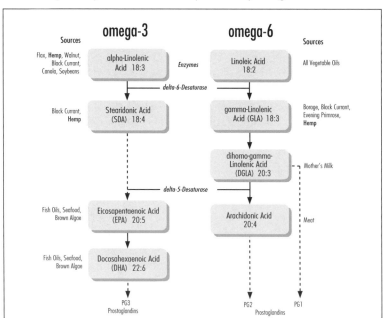

Omega-3 and omega-6 deficiencies: Because alpha-linolenic acid contains three double bonds, it oxidizes much faster than linoleic acid. This reduces the shelf life of oils high in alpha-linolenic acid, makes them unsuitable for frying, and less popular with oil producers and food processors. To raise the melting point and improve stability of these oils, they are routinely hardened or hydrogenated, which converts some of the unsaturated bonds into saturated ones. Also, plant-breeding efforts in recent years have focused on reducing the content of alpha-linolenic acid, for example in soybean oils. These trends, combined with the low content of alpha-linolenic acid in animal fat, are largely responsible for the deficiencies in omega-3 fatty acids in the typical North American diet.

Some people suffer from deficiencies in higher omega-3 and omega-6 metabolites and their prostaglandins, even if they eat sufficient quantities of EFAs. Here, the conversion of EFAs into higher PUFAs by the delta-6 desaturase enzyme is inhibited and requires supplementation. The primary omega-6 supplement is gamma-linolenic acid (GLA, 18:3 omega-6), found in high concentrations in the oils of evening primrose (7 to 9 percent), borage (18 to 24 percent), and black currant (15 to 18 percent).

popcorn • Caramelized topping •

The higher omega-3 fatty acids eicosapentaenoic acid (EPA) and docosa-hexaenoic acid (DHA) are usually supplied by fish oils. Unlike hemp oil, all of these oils are unsuitable for cooking and are available only as dietary supplements. Hemp oil contains low to moderate concentrations of GLA (1 to 4 percent) and stearidonic acid (18:4 omega-3, 0.5 to 2 percent). Thus, hemp oil is both a versatile food oil and a moderate supplement for both higher omega-6 and omega-3 fatty acids. Moreover, it provides these fatty acids typically in a favorable omega-6/omega-3 ratio of 3:1. Compared to the average ratio of 4:1 to 6:1 recommended by international health organizations, it adds a little more omega-3 and makes up for the omega-3 shortage in the rest of our food supply.

Cis- and trans-fatty acids: The double bonds of unsaturated fatty acids may occur in two different configurations, referred to as "Cis" and "Trans," respectively. Fatty acids in vegetable oils contain primarily cis-double bonds, causing their curved shape. High temperatures during refining, hydrogenation, and deep frying convert some of the double bonds into the trans configuration. A trans-bond makes a straighter molecule, similar to that of a saturated fatty acid. Clinical studies suggest that trans-fatty acids–similar to saturated fatty acids–increase the risk of cardiovascular disease and should therefore be limited in our diet. For nutritional purposes, they should therefore be grouped with saturated fatty acids rather than with unsaturated fatty acids. [2,5,6,7] Unrefined hemp oil contains few to no trans-fatty acids. Studies suggest that only a small fraction of cis-fatty acids is converted during frying and deep-frying. However, the high content of PUFAs and the presence of free fatty acids promotes formation of unhealthful oxidation products (see Chapter Five) during frying and renders hemp oil unsuitable for these uses.

The Composition of Hemp Oil
The fatty acid spectrum of hemp oil is at the heart of its nutritional benefits. In comparison to other unrefined edible oils, hemp oil features a very high percentage of EFAs — typically 75 percent, mostly in the form of omega-6 linoleic acid. A high proportion (15 to 25 percent) is alpha-linolenic acid, found in relevant quantities in only a few other commonly used cooking oils such as soybean or canola oil. (Flax oil, which contains more than 50 percent alpha-linolenic acid, is a valuable nutritional supplement but, for taste and stability reasons, not a good cooking oil.) The monounsaturated oleic acid contributes 10 to 15 percent, and total saturated fatty acids account for 9 to 11 percent of total fatty acid in hemp oil. In addition it contains, depending on variety, low percentages of several other PUFAs that play an important role in human metabolism. Most

notable are gamma-linolenic acid (GLA, 18:3 omega-6) and stearidonic acid (18:4 omega-3). The content of these "minor" fatty acids varies considerably with variety and growing conditions. Varieties adapted to Northern latitudes produce oils with higher concentrations of these fatty acids. For example, a Finnish variety has GLA and stearidonic acid levels of 4 and 2 percent, respectively — considerably higher than varieties from Central Europe and China. This demonstrates the large potential for improving the fatty-acid spectrum of hemp oil through breeding. Consequently, breeders in Europe and Canada are presently developing varieties with a higher oil yield and a GLA content of more than 6 percent.

Typical fatty-acid composition of unrefined vegetable oils

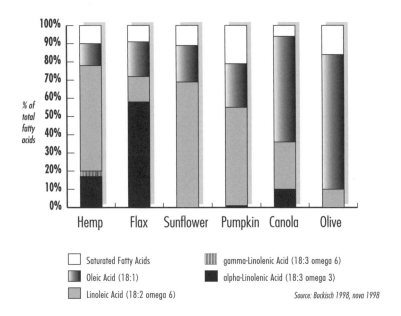

In cold-pressed, unrefined hemp oil, typically 1 to 2 percent of fatty acids are not connected to a glycerol backbone but float in the oil as *free fatty acids* (FFAs). In comparison, extra-virgin olive oil contains less than 1 percent FFAs. FFA levels are higher in immature or improperly handled seeds. At even higher concentrations, FFAs cause a scratchy feeling in the throat, as well as rapid smoking when the oil is pan-heated.

solutions • Coffee • Cold medicine

The fat-soluble compounds of the *vitamin E* complex, tocopherols and tocotrienols, are another important constituent of hemp oil. These are *antioxidants* that nature has added to oils to protect them from oxidation and rancidity (see Chapter Five). Conveniently, these antioxidants also provide health benefits, mainly by trapping excess free radicals in our body. In his comprehensive book on fats and nutrition, *Fats That Heal — Fats That Kill*, Udo Erasmus writes: ". . . free radicals serve vital, normal functions, but can also injure, age, degenerate, and kill our cells and tissues." Vitamin E has been shown to slow degenerative diseases and prevent or even cure thrombotic diseases. Recent research suggests that vitamin E may also inhibit brain-cell death in patients with Alzheimer's disease. Since many carcinogens act via free radicals, vitamin E can also reduce the corresponding cancer risk. Considering their promise of life extension, it comes as no surprise that antioxidants have become very popular as food supplements.

Hemp oil, compared to other cold-pressed and unrefined vegetable oils — olive, sunflower, canola — has a moderate to high content of vitamin E compounds. Typical levels are 100 to 150 milligrams per 100 grams of oil, predominantly in the form of gamma-tocopherol. This makes hemp oil a valuable source of vitamin E, with 1 to 2 tablespoons meeting daily requirements. Hulled seeds supply the same balanced fatty acids and antioxidants as hemp oil, wrapped up in valuable proteins (see Chapter Eight).

Finally, hemp oil also contains modest amounts of several other beneficial or even essential constituents. Worth mentioning are:

- *Phytosterols* that affect the absorption of cholesterol by the human body and cholesterol levels in the blood.
- *Phospholipids,* usually referred to as *lecithin.* They are essential for the integrity of cell membranes, support the breakup of ingested fats, and enhance fat utilization in the liver.
- *Carotenes* are precursors of vitamin A, necessary for regular growth and normal eyesight.
- Several *minerals,* including calcium, magnesium, and potassium.
  The presence of these nutrients in hemp oil further supports its reputation as a holistic food that provides a range of the nutrients our body needs — in a balanced and tasty blend. [3, 9, 13, 14, 18]

Good for Your Heart: Hemp Oil and the Choice of the Right Fats

Numerous clinical studies have shown that both oversupply of fat and deficiencies in some PUFAs are responsible for many common illnesses. These studies and surveys of dietary habits in Western countries have generated several widely accepted facts on fats: [2, 5, 6, 7]

• *Cookies* • *Crackers* • *Cream*

- The body needs fatty acids. They serve as building blocks for cell membranes and hormones and are the body's preferred way to store energy.

- Both saturated and unsaturated fatty acids are indispensable in some functions and detrimental in others. Thus there isn't one perfect fatty acid for everything.

- Too high a total fat intake causes obesity with all its related problems, including its strong indication as a cofactor in the high rate of cardiovascular disease in North America.

- High consumption of saturated fatty acids, overrepresented in a common North American diet of meat and fried foods, raises the level of undesirable blood cholesterol species. This accelerates deposition of arterial plaque, restricts blood flow, and increases the risk of heart attacks and strokes. Trans-fatty acids, formed during the hydrogenation and refining of vegetable oils, have a similar detrimental effect.

- A shift in your diet to unsaturated fatty acids-3 and omega-6s generally benefits high blood cholesterol levels: it lowers the "bad" LDL-cholesterol fraction while maintaining desirable HDL levels. This benefit is particularly well demonstrated for oleic acid, the main constituent in olive oil, and to a lesser degree for the omege-3 and omega 6 fatty acids. The reliance of the Mediterranean diet on olive oil is partly credited for the low occurrence of heart disease in these countries. There is also much evidence of help from exercise, less smoking, and a generally happier life.

- The two most common PUFAs, linoleic and alpha-linolenic aid, are simply essential, and are a source for all other fatty acids in our body. EFA deficiency may cause numerous illnesses. Our food usually contains sufficient omega-6s. However, as Dr. Andrew Weil states, "…the diets of most Americans are alarmingly deficient in omega-3s…," thus calling for a higher intake of foods rich in omega-3 fatty acids. (Though some studies have indicated that a high intake of linoleic acid may increase breast-cancer risk, these studies are fervently debated and were likely flawed by design.)

- A healthy body enzymatically converts the two EFAs into important, higher omega-3 and omega-6 acids and prostaglandins. People for whom this process is inhibited will suffer from deficiency symptoms, including skin disorders in sensitive individuals (omega-6) and illnesses of the nervous and cardiovascular systems (omega-3). These symptoms can often be cured by direct supplementation with therapeutic doses of higher omega-3 and omega-6 fatty acids (including GLA).

cheese • Cream soups •

With this in mind, health officials and nutritional experts in many countries agree on the following general rules regarding fat intake:

- Fat should be consumed in moderation. Only about 30 percent of our calories should come from fat, corresponding to about 70 grams for an average diet of 2,000 calories per day.
- Saturated, monounsaturated, and polyunsaturated fatty acids should each contribute about one-third of the total fat intake. Be moderate with food high in saturated fats (red meat, fried foods), look for prepared foods with low levels of saturated fats, and use several different vegetable oils for cooking, preferably cold-pressed olive, hemp, safflower, and walnut oils.
- Overall, omega-6 and omega-3 polyunsaturated fatty acids should be consumed in a typical ratio of 4:1 to 6:1. Thus, make sure your diet contains sufficient alpha-linolenic and other omega-3 fatty acids by including hemp oil, hulled hempseeds, and fish as a staple and—in the case of an omega-3 deficiency—flax oil, ground flaxseed, and possibly fish oil as supplements.
- Diets rich in PUFAs should also provide sufficient antioxidants in the form of vitamin E. Use cold-pressed oils, other foods high in antioxidants, or vitamin E supplements.

A Nutritionally Ideal Oil

- has a low content of saturated and trans-fatty acids,
- contains a high fraction of EFAs in a proportion close to an omega-6: omega-3 ratio of 4:1, possibly lower,
- provides small quantities of other longer-chain omega-3 and omega-6 fatty acids in which some people are deficient, as well as a good supply of vitamin E and phytosterols, and
- adds flavor to a wide variety of dishes.

Thus, consider cold-pressed hemp oil. It is not an all-purpose oil; because of its instability, it should not be used for frying. Rather, it is one of the most healthful "package deals" in vegetable oil available, and is a fine element in a balanced diet.

•   *Dessert   toppings*   •   *Detergents*   •

4

Nutritional and Therapeutic Uses of Hemp Oil

Extensive studies have demonstrated that many common illnesses are related to deficiencies or imbalances of specific fatty acids in the body. Symptoms are often related to a lack of omega-3 and omega-6 fatty acids and their derivatives, the prostaglandins (see Chapter Three). Most people eating a healthful diet—one that includes a balanced ratio of essential fatty acids (EFAs)—also have healthy skin and a strong immune system. Yet some individuals may experience shortages in specific fatty acids or their metabolites, due to dysfunctional enzyme systems or other inhibitions in their metabolic pathways caused by genetic, immune-system-related, or even environmental factors. It has been proven in several clinical studies that dietary supplementation with EFAs or their metabolites (such as GLA) will often prevent or even cure these illnesses.[2, 7, 10, 14]

Since hemp oil contains both EFAs in a desirable balance and provides two of the EFA metabolites, it is a good resource for the prevention and treatment of certain illnesses. Further, unlike evening primrose, flax, or fish oils, it provides these benefits as a "functional food" or "nutraceutical," not as a dietary supplement. However, those who prefer to take their hemp oil as a dietary supplement will find gel caps readily available. Since most hemp oil on the market today contains less than 3 percent GLA, daily GLA doses above 600 milligrams become increasingly difficult to supply. The following illnesses respond to treatment with omega-6 and omega-3 fatty acids.

Atopic Eczema (Neurodermitis) and Psoriasis

Patients with atopic eczema suffer from agonizing itching, especially at night. Because of low activity of the perspiratory and sebaceous glands, the skin feels very dry and brittle. Atopic eczema, like psoriasis, is characterized by a high water loss through the skin. A deficiency in omega-6 polyunsaturated fatty acids (PUFAs) is associated with these diseases. One theory is that low enzymatic activity results in slower conversion of linoleic acid to GLA, causing a prostaglandin imbalance.

Dips • Dressings • Dry mixes •

Clinical trials with GLA supplementation have demonstrated gradual improvement in atopic eczema symptoms. Patients required considerably less use of anti-itching and antihistamine drugs. Hemp oil, due to its moderate GLA content, may assist in the prevention and treatment of this disease. The daily oral dose found to improve skin conditions over a twelve-week period corresponds to about four teaspoons of hemp oil, which is easily incorporated into the diet.

The external use of salves and creams containing hemp oil further supports the barrier function of the skin, helps relieve skin itching, and aids in the recovery of atopic eczema patients (see Chapter Six). Omega-6 fatty acids are also involved in regulating water loss through the outer layer of the skin, the epidermis. It was shown that skin conditions in atopic eczema patients improved after repeated external application of an ointment containing GLA.

Acne
PUFAs have well-known anti-inflammatory properties, and skin creams containing omega-6 fatty acids have been found effective in the therapeutic treatment of acne skin conditions. Hemp oil's high omega-6 content can therefore be beneficially used in skin-care products for skin with acne problems.

Cardiovascular Disease
Most cardiovascular disease is caused by the formation of arterial plaque —fatty deposits on the interior walls of the blood vessels that, over time, harden and impede blood flow in a condition known as **atherosclerosis**. This process may eventually block blood flow and cause a stroke or a heart attack. LDL (the "bad") cholesterol, a sticky lipid present in the blood, is a major contributor to arterial plaque. Among other factors, such as smoking and stress, the intake of saturated fatty acids contributes to high blood LDL levels. Dietary treatment of patients with daily doses of linoleic acid and GLA (omega-6) equivalent to five teaspoons of hemp oil was shown to rapidly decrease elevated blood levels of both LDL cholesterol and total cholesterol, thereby reducing the risk of thrombosis. Another study showed that omega-3 fatty acids significantly reduced the risk of sudden cardiac death among survivors of heart attacks. Thus, the replacement of other dietary oils and fats with hemp oil will help reduce the risk of atherosclerosis and other cardiovascular diseases.

Rheumatoid Arthritis and Other Inflammatory Diseases
Patients with rheumatoid arthritis suffer from joints that are chronically inflamed, causing pain, immobility, and eventual deformation of the

joints. Some fatty acids, including GLA, and their metabolites, the prostaglandins, have well-known anti-inflammatory and immune-system-stimulating properties. Daily oral administration of 1.2 to 1.4 grams of GLA over a period of twelve weeks was found to reduce the symptoms of rheumatoid arthritis significantly, without causing side effects. Clinical studies have also shown that intake of omega-3 fatty acids has anti-inflammatory effects in the treatment of such illnesses as chronic bladder infection and inflammatory bowel diseases such as ulcerative colitis and Crohn's disease.

Osteoporosis

Osteoporosis, the gradual decay of the bones with age, is caused by a loss of bone substance, particularly calcium. Back pain, height loss, a curved spine, and easily fracturing bones are its effects. Osteoporosis is also associated with the calcification of arteries and kidneys — a frequent cause of vascular deaths, particularly in women.

Studies have shown that dietary supplementation with EFAs increases calcium absorption from the gut, reduces urinary excretion of calcium, increases calcium deposition in bones, and enhances bone-collagen synthesis, thereby improving bone strength. The effects were attributed to an increase in circulating prostaglandins, metabolites of the EFAs. Supplementation with the higher omega-6 fatty acid GLA was even more effective. Hemp oil, with its moderate content of GLA and well-balanced ratio of EFAs, helps to prevent osteoporosis when included in the diet.

PMS and Menopause

PMS, or premenstrual syndrome, affects many women before the onset of their monthly period. It can cause depression, irritability, swelling of the breasts, and painful muscular tension. Studies show that women with PMS suffer from a disorder in the metabolism of fatty acid that also slows the conversion of linoleic acid to GLA and prostaglandins. A daily dose of 150-200 milligrams GLA (corresponding to one teaspoon of hemp oil) over a twelve-week period significantly improved PMS-related symptoms in clinical studies.

Menopausal symptoms such as dry skin, hot flashes, night sweats, mood swings, and drying of the vaginal and bladder mucous membranes may also be alleviated by dietary EFA supplementation.

Other Therapeutic Benefits

A dysfunctional fatty-acid metabolism also seems to contribute to the following diseases. The potential benefits of EFAs and higher omega-3 and omega-6 fatty acids in their treatment require further study.

• *Falafel* • *Fish bait* •

Multiple sclerosis (MS), a chronic neurological autoimmune disease, occurs more frequently in the northern industrialized regions of the world, where, incidentally, the diet also includes a disproportionately low ratio of unsaturated fats. Studies have suggested a link between abnormal EFA metabolism and progression of the MS symptoms, possibly due to a defective enzyme system. MS patients may be unable to convert EFAs to the higher PUFAs. Some studies indicate that dietary supplementation with EFAs or GLA will lead to improvements.

Diabetes, a common endocrine disorder, stems from an inadequate production of insulin, the major blood-sugar-regulating hormone. As one effect, the resulting high blood-sugar levels make EFAs in tissues unavailable, causing an EFA deficiency. Diabetes patients often suffer from neuropathies—tingling or numbness in their feet caused by impaired blood circulation. Studies showed alleviation of these symptoms with daily doses of 360 milligrams GLA (corresponding to 2 to 3 teaspoons of hemp oil).

Compared to healthy tissue, **cancer** tissue and cells have lower contents of GLA and other higher omega-6 PUFAs studies suggest that cancer treatment may be assisted by the administration of linoleic acid and GLA.

Further research on dietary supplementation of EFAs, GLA, and other omega-3 and omega-6 PUFAs suggests improvements in the treatment of **chronic depression, postpartum depression, attention deficit disorder, and schizophrenic psychosis,** among other afflictions.

This brief list shows that hemp oil's fatty-acid spectrum may prevent or assist in curing a number of common diseases when taken as part of the normal diet. Patients suffering seriously from any of the listed illnesses should discuss the therapeutic use of hemp oil, or other oils high in specific PUFAs, with a medical professional.

• *F i s h   f o o d* • *F l o u r* •

5

The Production and Handling of High-Quality Hemp Oil

Most food oils on supermarket shelves are produced by crushing and extracting oil seeds with hexane, a petroleum-derived solvent. This method maximizes the yield of the oil, which is then mechanically and chemically refined. Refining removes undesirable free fatty acids, off flavors, and other oxidation products, thereby increasing shelf life. Yet refining also removes the compounds that give oil its characteristic flavor and color, as well as other valuable ingredients such as vitamins A and E, lecithin, and minerals. Because these solvent-extracted and refined commodity oils lack character and valuable trace substances, cold-pressed and unrefined olive, walnut, and safflower oils are lately gaining shelf space.

Most cold-pressed oils are produced by expeller-pressing seeds while keeping the oil temperature at the outlet typically below 130° F (55° C). If unrefined, these oils retain the characteristic aroma of the seeds and much of their fat-soluble vitamins, other antioxidants, and minor constituents. While the low pressing temperature reduces the oil yield, it also minimizes oxidation and the formation of off flavors.

Hemp Oil: Handle With Care

The high EFA content of hemp oil is the main contributor to its nutritional value. Yet it also causes instability, and necessitates careful quality control throughout the production process. The instability of hemp oil is largely due to the reactivity of the triple-unsaturated alpha-linolenic acid. Its reaction with free radicals and oxygen creates numerous oxidation products—some merely bad tasting, some toxic. This gradual oxidation of fatty acids is called rancidification. Oils turn rancid faster if exposed to light, heat, and oxygen. Rancid oils are detected by their unpleasant flavor, ranging from painty to buttery.

Fortunately, nature provides oil seeds rich in polyunsaturated fatty acids with a built-in protection from oxidation: antioxidants. Vegetable oils contain several antioxidants belonging to the vitamin E group (see Chapter Three). These capture free radicals in the oil, responsible for initiating the oxidation of fatty acids. Yet, despite hemp oil's moderate to high vitamin E content, it is very sensitive to damage by oxidation, thus requiring careful handling and protection from field to kitchen.

Since oil composition and taste can vary considerably, selecting the right hemp variety is the first oil-quality control measure.

Quality Parameters for Hemp Oil

For characterization of the quality of oil and its oxidative stability, the following parameters are commonly used:

Free Fatty Acids (FFAs): The free-fatty-acid content is measured in percent (as oleic acid). In unrefined hemp oil, a content of 1 to 2 percent FFAs is acceptable. Refining achieves FFA contents of less than 0.03 percent.

Peroxide Value (PV): The PV measures the concentration of peroxidized fatty acids. It is given in milliequivalent oxygen per kilogram of oil (meq/kg). The PV for unrefined hemp oil is typically 2 to 6 meq/kg, and can be reduced to below 0.03 meq/kg by refining.

Quality Control From Field to Bottle

The quality and taste of hemp oil is also determined by the growing, harvesting, and handling of the seeds. Crops with a high number of green, immature seeds will, unless thoroughly screened, produce a greener, grassy-tasting oil with a higher free-fatty-acid content. Expeditious drying of the seeds after harvesting to less than 10 percent moisture is essential to avoid sprouting and molds. The drying temperature must be kept below 105° F (40° C) in order to avoid oozing of the oil, which would expose it to oxygen and accelerate rancidification. Subsequent thorough cleaning removes dirt, as well as traces of THC present in the flowers.

The pressing temperature during expeller pressing strongly impacts the yield, color, and taste of hemp oil. Oil yield increases with temperature, yet at crushing temperatures above 120° F (50° C), higher amounts of chlorophyll in the hulls are dissolved into the oil, making it both greener and grassier. Crushing at temperatures of less than 120° F generally produces a nuttier-tasting, clearer oil. In order to minimize rancidification and maintain the good flavor of the oil, unrefined hemp oil is routinely pressed and bottled under a nitrogen atmosphere. It is sold in tinted glass or dark plastic bottles to protect it from light.

The oxidation of vegetable oils is avoided or reduced by natural antioxidants, such as vitamin E, present in seeds. Hemp oil contains comparatively high concentrations of antioxidants, particularly of gamma-tocopherol. If further antioxidants are needed, for example in body-care products, the use of natural antioxidants, such as vitamin E or extracts from rosemary, grapefruit seeds, or green tea, should be considered. Refined oil usually requires additional antioxidants, since refining removes a large fraction of the naturally present tocopherols.

The user also has a say in quality control. Bottles of hemp oil should be stored only in the refrigerator, and the oil consumed within six months at most. This is the most effective way to avoid rancidification. Finally, the heating of unrefined hemp oil to temperatures above 320° F (160° C) during cooking will cause smoking and will compromise taste and quality (see Chapter Nine).

Several emerging crushing technologies promise to combine the taste and nutritional value of cold-pressed oils with the higher yield of hexane-extracted oil. Technologies may involve the use of more selective, environmentally less detrimental solvents, such as carbon dioxide and ethanol, or mechanical means, such as a modified centrifugal separator. Pending stricter regulatory limits on the emission of hexane residues from oil processors may accelerate the implementation of these technologies.

The instability of hemp oil is the price we pay for its high nutritional value. Yet careful harvesting, crushing, bottling, and usage will maintain taste and quality and help to avoid unpleasant surprises.[5, 14]

Storage Tips

- Light and oxygen are natural enemies of unsaturated fatty acids. Keep hemp oil in tightly sealed bottles made of dark glass or plastic.
- Higher temperatures accelerate fat oxidation. Store the oil in the refrigerator.
- Oxidization and chemical reactions happen over time. Use the oil within a few months of opening the bottle.

Hair conditioners • Hard cheeses

6

Healing Body-Care Products

While body-care products containing hemp oil have only recently entered mainstream markets, their use dates back into antiquity. In the past, hemp oil was widely used to manufacture soothing skin-care lotions and a soft, greenish soap (see Chapter One). This oil's proclaimed benefits in body-care products have sparked much experimentation. A wide range of products containing hemp oil are now available, including soaps, shampoos, conditioners, hand creams, shower gels, baby creams, massage oils, lipsticks, lip balms, and moisturizing body lotions.

Hemp oil provides several benefits for our skin and for the environment. As we have said, more than 75 percent of the fatty acids in hemp oil are polyunsaturated fatty acids (PUFAs), known for their excellent emollient and lubricating properties. Further, in hemp oil a high percentage of these PUFAs are the omega-6 fatty acids linoleic acid and gamma-linolenic acid (GLA). Clinical studies have shown that these specific fatty acids can alleviate or even remedy skin problems, such as dry skin, when applied externally. Finally, even nonorganically grown hemp usually doesn't require the use of pesticides. Thus, consumers need not be concerned about the potential presence of pesticide residues in oil and body-care products or in the environment.

Plant Oils for Skin Care

Including in the diet oils rich in omega-3 and omega-6 fatty acids has proven preventive and therapeutic effects for the skin. For skin-care applications, we can rely as much on the purely physical emollient, lubricant, and moisturizing effects of fatty acids as on the well-established restorative effects of specific PUFAs. Clinical tests have shown specifically that the dry-skin defects—scaling or cracking—caused by dietary essential fatty acid (EFA) deficiency can be reversed by skin-care products containing omega-6 fatty acids. The antiinflammatory properties of PUFAs can further aid in the healing of minor skin abrasions and acne.

Hummus • Lip balm • Lipstick •

How Our Skin Works

To better understand the benefits of essential fatty acids (EFAs) and hemp oil to our skin, let's look at the skin's structure and numerous functions. The skin acts not only as a sensory organ and temperature control, it also has important barrier functions: it protects the body from excessive water loss and from penetration by foreign substances and pathogens such as bacteria and viruses. A major function of skin-care products is to enhance, preserve, or restore this barrier.

The health of our skin depends largely on the presence and retention of water. Moisture retention is mostly provided by the epidermis, the topmost and thinnest layer of the skin. The actual "vapor barrier" is the stratum corneum, the outer layer of the epidermis. It is composed of, and continuously rebuilt from, dying and dead cells that gradually flake off the skin surface. These cells are held together—just like bricks cemented by mortar—by lipids, i.e., fat-like substances including sterols, free fatty acids, and ceramides.

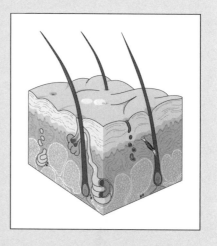

The weakening or failure of this natural barrier leads to dry skin. This process is promoted by sun, dry air, excessive use of soaps, shower gels, or other detergents, and organic solvents with a strong degreasing action. The slowdown of cell metabolism with age or diabetes is another contributor. All these factors result in changes in the lipid composition of the epidermis and reduced moisture-retention capability. The skin becomes thinner, facilitating increased water loss. The result is dry, brittle skin with a rough and unpleasant feel. A ceramide that is of critical importance to the moisture control of the skin is made from the omega-6 lineolic acid. This partly explains the benefits of omega-6 fatty acids in body care and therapeutic applications.

The metabolic slowdown associated with aging also leads to dry-skin conditions. Slower metabolism and growth of cells in the basal layer of the epidermis also causes with a decline of ceramide content. Both contribute to the formation of wrinkles and overall skin aging. The application of omega-6 fatty acids in skin-care products may partially compensate for the lower ceramide levels in the skin and the resulting aging effects. Another obvious sign of age—brown liver spots—cannot be prevented by skin care, but only by a diet rich in EFAs.

Sensitivity to ingredients in skin-care products is a major consumer concern. So far, manufacturers and users of hemp body-care products have reported no allergic reactions to hemp oil. Another concern, the absorption of THC via the skin—is also unsubstantiated (see Chapter Seven).[8, 14]

Oxidative Stability in Body-Care Products

Once a skin-care product is applied, its lipids become exposed to light and oxygen. The subsequent, unavoidable oxidation is catalyzed or accelerated by UV-light-absorbing photosensitizers in the oil, such as the green chlorophyll. Removing pigments from the oil through refining processes increases photooxidative stability. Thus, some manufacturers of skin-care products use refined hemp oil in their formulations. Refining creates a colorless, odorless oil, more acceptable to mainstream markets than dark-green unrefined oil. Antioxidants are also commonly added to body-care products containing hemp oil. They reduce photosensitivity and increase shelf life, particularly of opened products.

Hemp Oil for Massage

Massage therapy is becoming ever more popular as an important element of holistic health care. EFA-rich oils are readily absorbed by the skin, thus the EFA-rich hemp oil makes an excellent ingredient for massage oils.

A good oil blend for massage therapy is one third hemp oil, one third olive oil, and one third avocado, sesame, or jojoba oil. Adding rosemary essential oil and/or ascorbic acids in small amounts will help increase shelf life.

Use massage oils and body lotions with moderation. Too much of a good thing will not only stain your clothes, but oxidation of PUFA-rich oils on your skin may cause a sticky feeling and a paint-like odor.

Hemp Oil in Hair-Care Products

When used in hair-care products, hemp oil provides important benefits. In shampoos and conditioners, these result primarily from the therapeutic effects of hemp oil's fatty-acid composition on the scalp. It gives relief from the dry, itchy feeling of a scaly scalp. Since the hair itself consists of dead cells, its exposure to sun, blow-dryer heat, and chemicals for bleaching, coloring, or perms gradually makes it dull and brittle. In hair-care products, hemp oil's lipids make hair more manageable, add to body, and enhance shine.

Natural Cleaning Agents From Hemp Oil

In most of the above-mentioned body-care products, hemp oil's function is the lubrication of the skin with PUFAs. The other potential body-care application for hemp oil is as a raw material in innovative, eco-friendly biodegradable detergents or cleaning agents. A German manufacturer now offers an effective, skin-friendly detergent made from hemp oil or sunflower oil and yeast. It is well suited for shampoos, liquid soaps, and foam-bath formulations.

From an environmental standpoint, such plant-oil-based cleaning products are far preferable to petrochemical detergents. Once they go down the drain, they biodegrade rapidly, lessening the burden on wastewater treatment plants, rivers, fish, and other wildlife.

Mayonnaise • Meat alternatives •

7

The THC Issue

In response to the growing use of hemp foods, health agencies and the media in Western countries have questioned whether these foods are safe for human consumption. At issue is the possibility that hempseeds and hemp oil contain trace quantities of delta-9-tetrahydrocannabinol (THC), the major psychoactive ingredient of marijuana. Oils pressed from the whole seeds of Chinese or European industrial-hemp varieties typically contain 5 to 20 parts per million (ppm) or milligrams per kilogram of THC. The levels in other hemp foods are even lower.

Hempseeds themselves contain no THC nor any of the other cannabinoids present in marijuana. Rather, these compounds are produced in glands of the female flowers, whose sticky resins may leave traces of THC on the seed hulls. Studies have shown that farming hemp varieties with a lower THC content and thorough cleaning of the seeds are effective in reducing THC levels in oil to below 5 ppm. Hulled seeds contain even less THC (below 2 ppm). Thus, hemp-food producers now emphasize proper seed cleaning or the use of hulled seeds.[12, 15]

Such low THC levels pose no risk of involuntary intoxication. Based on the review of scientific studies on the effects of THC, the Swiss government has set a 50 ppm limit for THC in hemp oil and a limit of 5 ppm for other foods, such as baked goods. Health Canada has set a general 10 ppm limit for materials from industrial hemp. Other European countries and the United States Food and Drug Administration have yet to adopt standards.

A recent comprehensive study by the German nova-Institute[15] has evaluated toxicological data on the potential risk caused by the ingestion of THC with oil and other foods. Based on available toxicological data, the Institute has recommended THC limits somewhat lower than the Swiss ones, ranging from 0.3 percent for nonalcoholic beverages to 20 ppm for hemp oil. These limits provide an ample margin of safety from psychoactive effects, even when hemp foods are consumed in large quantities. The study also suggests that the absorption of THC from hemp-oil-based skin-care products is not effective and will not cause any relevant uptake. A summary of the study is available at the Web site of the

North American Industrial Hemp Council (www.naihc.org). A copy of the full report can be ordered from HEMPTECH (see resources section).[15, 17]

Hemp Foods and Drug Testing

In several recent cases, it was found that the ingestion of low amounts of THC with hemp foods may result in a positive urine test for drugs. In these instances, civil and military courts have cleared defendants of drug charges. This has caused some confusion for the drug-testing industry, as well as the Drug Enforcement Agency and the Department of Defense. The real issue is the high sensitivity of these tests and their pervasive use.

Up until 1998, most U.S. hemp foods and oil were manufactured from Chinese seeds. These were collected from wild varieties that have a higher THC content than varieties grown in Europe and Canada. The last remaining DEA-permitted sterilization facility, which steam-sterilized all imported hempseeds (including the Chinese seeds), closed its doors in 1998. Now, in 1999, food manufacturers import seeds, hulled seeds, flour, and oil from Canada and Europe. The seeds are from registered hemp varieties with a low THC content (0.03 percent or less), and are well-cleaned before use. Thus, THC residues in today's hemp foods are at such low levels that the risk of positive drug testing is virtually eliminated.

That hemp food will usually not result in a positive urine test was recently demonstrated in Kentucky. Ten local dignitaries met at the White Light Diner for a "hemp banquet"—dishes made with hemp oil and hulled seeds—and took a urine test before and after. None of them tested positive. Overall, there is plenty of evidence that actual THC levels in hemp foods pose no risk of involuntary intoxication or other health dangers.[15]

How Much THC Does It Take?

Scientific studies suggest that a single dose of 5 mg THC causes no acute intoxicating or chronic detrimental effects in a person weighing 150 pounds. To ingest such a dose, one must theroretically consume
- 1 pint (500 milligrams) of hemp oil containing 10 ppm THC, or
- 5 pounds (2.5 kilograms) of hulled hempseeds at 2 ppm THC.

Even for the most enthusiastic hemp-foods fan, the ingestion of such quantities would be a challenge.

Muffins • Nondairy cheese •

8

The New Hemp Foods

While hemp oil has been the first edible hempseed product to reappear, hulled hempseeds, or hemp nuts, are rapidly finding their way into our diets. They share the health benefits of hemp oil and are also a nutritious source of protein, vitamins, and minerals.

The importation of whole seeds into the United States has been complicated by the seeds' legally required sterilization, aimed at preventing viable seeds from growing into hemp plants. Even sprouting a few hempseeds for your salad from low-THC varieties would be an illegal act. Seeds are steam-sterilized for fifteen minutes at 212° F (100° C), which will crack some seeds, thus reducing their shelf life.

Whole seeds of good quality have been available in the U.S. for several years. Applications for whole seeds and seed meal include their increasing use in the mash of hemp beers, in snacks, and in baked goods. A tasty and healthful way to enjoy them is slightly roasted and salted— a popular snack at parties. Coffee companies are also using roasted hempseeds to make a more healthful coffee blend.

Yet the pesky hulls, which like to stick between the teeth, have annoyed gourmets. So hempseed suppliers developed methods to hull the seeds. The small size and tight fit of the hull made hempseed hulling a challenge. Yet, since 1997 hulled hempseeds, originally from Germany, have been available in North America. Canadian firms, following their first commercial hemp crop in 1998, now also export a range of hempseed products, including hulled seeds, meal, flour, nut butter, hulls, and oil.

Hempseeds as a Protein Source

Compared to hemp oil, little research has been conducted on hemp protein, but it will receive more attention with the increasing use of hemp foods. Although data on hemp's amino-acid spectrum is limited, it suggests the following general conclusions. Whole and hulled hempseeds contain about 25 and 35 percent protein, respectively. The protein contains all nine essential amino acids and features a high content of the two sulfur-containing amino acids methionine and cysteine, usually underrepresented in vegetable proteins. Depending somewhat on variety, hemp

Dietary Protein

Proteins in the human body serve many functions, acting as enzymes, antibodies, and structural components of tissues, hormones, and blood proteins, to name just a few. The main function of dietary protein is to supply amino acids for the growth and maintenance of body tissue. Digestion disassembles proteins into their basic building blocks, the amino acids, which are subsequently reassembled into the various body proteins.

Nine of the twenty amino acids are considered essential because the human body cannot manufacture them. In human nutrition, proteins with a high content of methionine and cysteine are desirable as a source of dietary sulfur. *Food proteins are considered complete when they contain all nine essential amino acids in a sufficient quantity and ratio to meet the body's needs.* Such complete proteins are found in meat, milk, eggs, and algae. Most proteins from individual plants are incomplete, yet a combination of complementary proteins in a vegetarian diet can adequately supply all essential amino acids in the right ratio. Important for the value of a protein is not just its composition but its digestibility. It depends on the protein's structure and on the presence or absence of inhibitory compounds sometimes found in soy and some vegetables.

protein provides a very attractive amino-acid spectrum and nutritional value, possibly superior to that of soy protein. Hempseed protein also contains high proportions of glutamic acid, an important neurotransmitter often in short supply under stress.

About 65 percent of the total protein in hempseed occurs as the easily digestible storage protein edestin. While several oilseeds contain antinutritional factors such as trypsin inhibitors in soybeans, none of these occur in hempseeds. All in all, hempseed proteins contribute to a complete and balanced diet.

N o n d a i r y   m i l k   •   N u t   b u t t e r

Nutty Foods

The hulling of hempseeds provides three important advantages:

- The crunchy hull is removed in a mechanical, nonheating process. This yields a tasty, nutty, highly nutritional and versatile meat.
- Hulled seeds can no longer germinate. Thus the seeds and their products can be imported into the U.S. without sterilization.
- Hulling removes most THC that may have been left on the hulls after cleaning. Thus, hulled seeds contain virtually no THC (less than 2 ppm), thus making irrelevant the issues discussed in Chapter Seven.

Hulled hempseeds are slightly larger than sesame seeds, taste like sunflower seeds, and offer a full range of culinary applications. A quick, low-temperature pan toasting brings out the nutty flavor in these foods...tasty enough to make you want to munch on them straight.

Hulled hempseeds—or hemp nuts—are perfectly suited to replace soy or rice protein in nondairy beverages (soy milk, chocolate drinks), frozen desserts (ice creams and sorbets), tofu, and cheeses. While today's nuts are a bit small for some applications, the breeding of varieties with larger seeds will make hempseeds more competitive with peanuts and cashews in the future.

How to Use Hulled Seeds

- Grind them into nut butter for use in sandwiches, hummus, tahini, sauces, and salad dressings.
- Sprinkle them, plain or lightly toasted, on pasta, salads, cooked grains, and breakfast cereals.
- Use them to give body to soups, stews, sauces, and gravies.
- Bake them into breads and pastries.
- Have them in candy bars, nutritional bars, and other snacks.
- Enjoy them in tofu and in non-dairy milk, cheese, and ice cream.
- Bread fish with toasted ground hulled seeds, adding them at the very end to prevent the ground seeds from overheating.

For more ideas, see the list of hempseed foods at the bottom of each page.

Hempseed Meal: Bake It, Brew It, Feed It to Your Animals

Hempseeds provide yet another raw material for food: the meal or seed-cake that remains after oil crushing. The meal from cold-pressed whole seeds consists mainly of protein (about 30 percent) and hulls, and 5 to 10

HempNut, Inc.

Hulled hempseeds

percent fat. It can be ground into baking flour that can replace some of the wheat or rye flour in recipes. Since it contains no gluten—the "glue" present in other cereal flours—and has a stronger taste, no more than 20 percent of the flour called for in a recipe should be replaced by hempseed flour. German hemp-oil producers increasingly sell their hemp flour to bakeries. Hemp meal is also used by microbreweries as an ingredient of the mash, giving additional body and flavor to beers. Because of their high PUFA content, meal and flour are sensitive to rancidity and need to be handled and stored carefully.

Crushing hulled seeds for oil results in a lighter, nuttier-tasting oil. The remaining seedcake contains no hulls and has an even higher protein content of more than 50 percent, making it a good ingredient for protein drinks, baking flour, and dairy substitutes.

One of the obvious applications for hemp meal is its use as animal feed. It has all of the amino acids present in the seeds, and 75 percent of the residual oil is essential fatty acids (EFAs). Hemp's content of sulfur-containing amino acids is superior to that of other oilseed cakes. The results of feeding tests conducted with horses, cattle, sheep, pigs, catfish, and chickens suggest that hemp meal can be used beneficially as animal feed in combination with other protein feedstocks. Because of its comparatively low lysine and total-protein content, it needs to be blended according to the dietary needs of the given animals.[9, 14]

O i l • *O i l   c a p s u l e s* • *P a n c a k e s*

Its high content of omega-3 alpha-linolenic acid also qualifies hempseed as a pet-food additive. The U.S. pet-food industry currently uses more than 5,000 tons of ground flaxseed per year, in order to improve the ratio of omega-3 and omega-6 fatty acids and thus reduce risks of dry skin and allergic reactions.[6]

The Future of Hemp Foods

Hemp foods are still in the early stages of product development. It is indeed an exciting time as these new foods start to appear on the shelves of natural-food stores. The attention paid to hemp foods is increasing due to their diversity of uses, their good taste and nutritional profile, and the growing interest in eco-friendly products. Yet hemp foods must meet a few challenges before they can expand beyond their current niches.

To start with, the prices of hempseeds and their products will gradually have to come down. This will be accomplished by increasing sales volumes and the resulting economies of scale in farming, processing, and distribution. More efficient processing and marketing of hemp fibers and hurds will also be crucial, so that farmers can reduce the cost of seeds.

Improving the properties of hempseeds through breeding will make them more competitive in several areas. Larger seeds will improve the efficiency of the hulling process, thus making hulled seeds more cost-competitive. Breeding varieties for a higher content of specific fatty acids such as GLA will make hemp oil more competitive as a food supplement, while raising the antioxidant levels in hempseeds will increase shelf life of hemp oil and foods. Finally, more hempseed research is needed in such areas as additional potential health benefits, the nature and effects of phytosterols, and the amino acid spectrum of different varieties.

Increasingly, hempseed will replace beans, nuts, oil seeds, grains, and dairy products in numerous foods. By successfully meeting the challenges mentioned above, hempseeds and their oil may well become a main staple for the expanding natural-foods industry.

9

Cooking With Hemp:
Tips and Delicious Recipes

Hempseeds and hemp oil are different from other seed-foods, mainly because of their high content of polyunsaturated fatty acids (PUFAs). The following tips will help you to fully enjoy the nutritional and taste potential of hemp foods and avoid disappointments.[11] As we've said, hempseed is recognized in the United States as a legal commodity as long as the seed is nonviable. Thus oil, flour, seed meal, hulled seeds, hulls, nut butter, and steam-sterilized or toasted whole seeds may be imported and consumed in the U.S. Requirements in most other Western countries are even more lenient.

Hemp Oil
Cold-pressed, unrefined hemp oil is light green, with a nutty, grassy flavor. Oil from hulled seeds is lighter in color, more nutty, and less grassy. Since refined hemp oil is clear but has no flavor and few nutrients, unrefined oil is preferable for food purposes.

Uses: Hemp oil can be used in dips, spreads, marinades, and salad dressings. It is suitable for quick sautéing, as long as moisture prevents high temperatures but not for frying—especially not deep-frying. It can replace, or be combined with your favorite oils, such as olive, walnut, or safflower.

Storage: Hemp oil is sensitive to oxygen, heat, and light. Bottles should be stored in a dark, cool place (the refrigerator is best) and used within six months.

Whole Hempseeds
Uses: Whole hempseeds can be toasted as snacks or ground for flour. Viable (unsterilized) hempseeds can be soaked and sprouted. However, viable seeds are not presently available in the U.S.

Storage: Before use, keep whole hempseeds cool, preferably in the refrigerator. Shelf life varies with seed quality, but they should be good for about a year.

Washing: Even well-cleaned seeds will contain small amounts of dirt and "bad seeds." Pour 1 to 2 pounds (1/2 to 1 kilogram) of seeds into a vessel in plenty of water. Dirt and cracked seeds will sink to the bottom, while the good seeds will float. Scoop them out with a spoon and drain them in a colander.

Toasting: Heat a pan on medium heat. Add a few handfuls of the well-drained seeds. Stir the seeds with a spoon or shake the pan frequently, to avoid overheating them. Burnt seeds turn black and bitter. The seeds are done when they start popping in large numbers. Add sea salt or other seasonings (like vegetable salt, soy sauce, or chili powder) for flavor. Store the toasted seeds in the refrigerator.

Hulled Hempseeds

These golden nuts are rapidly gaining popularity, thanks to their versatility and the absence of hulls. They look like sesame seeds and taste like sunflower seeds. Hulled seeds still contain small bits of hull and a few immature seeds. This unwanted content will be further reduced as larger seeds and improved technologies are developed.

Uses: Hulled hempseeds can be used as snacks (bars and nutballs), for baking (bread, cakes and cookies), sprinkled on salads or granola, and added to soups, stews, sauces, and dips.

Storage: Hulled hempseeds can easily turn rancid if they are not properly stored. Keep them dry, cool, and away from light. Once opened, they are best kept in the refrigerator. An opened container of hulled hempseeds in the refrigerator keeps several months.

Toasting: Hulled hempseeds are especially delicious when lightly and carefully toasted in a pan on top of the stove for about a minute. Careful with the heat: too much will make the seeds dark and bitter.

Nut Butter

Uses: Nut butter can be used as a butter substitute on breads, to make dips and spreads, or to add body to soups and sauces. The ground, hulled seeds (no oil added) are also quite versatile for cooking.

Preparation: Use either raw or lightly toasted hulled seed. Grind them in a coffee grinder or blender. The resulting fat-rich flour needs added oil to make it spreadable, whereas a Champion juicer produces a nut butter that needs no oil. Commercially made hemp butter is also available for purchase.

Storage: Store your nut butter in a closed jar in the refrigerator. Unless routinely left open on the breakfast table, it will keep for a few months . . . if it lasts that long!

Pilafs • Pita bread • Pralines

Hempseed Hulls

The hulling process yields great quantities of high-fiber hulls that have a protein content of about 10 percent.

Uses: Hemp hulls can be used in protein/fiber drinks in the same way that powdered walnut shells are used. They can also be included in animal feed.

Hemp Flour

The flour is the finely ground seed meal that remains after hempseeds are crushed for oil. It typically contains 5 to 10 percent oil; the rest is protein and hulls.

Uses: Hemp flour is best used in baked goods as a supplement to wheat or rye flours. Because it contains no gluten (the "glue" in other flours) and has its own characteristic flavor, replace no more than 20 percent of the flour called for in your recipes.

Storage: Hemp flour turns rancid fast. Keep it dry and cool, preferably in the freezer or refrigerator, and it may last for a few months.

Hemp Milk and Cheese Products

Uses: Non-dairy milk and cheese products are made from either whole or hulled hempseeds and can replace any dairy, soy-protein, or rice-protein-based materials.

Storage: Keep them in the refrigerator.

Where to Buy Hemp Foods, Seeds, and Oil

Hemp oil is found in the refrigerated sections of natural food markets. Ready-made hemp food products are available at natural food stores and supermarkets or by mail order. Hempseeds, whole and hulled, are mainly obtained via mail order from growers and distributors. Check the Resources section for information, or visit www.hemp-foods.com for an up-to-date address list.

• *Pretzels* • *Protein powder* •

Hemp-Food Recipes

The following basic recipes are meant to inspire your own experimentations with hempseeds or hemp oil. Use your culinary creativity, and remember that the toasting of hulled hemseeds for flavor is optional.

Toasted Hempseed Snack

1 cup whole, washed (see page 46) or hulled hempseeds
sea salt

Toast the seeds slowly at a low temperature, so they don't turn black. Add a pinch of salt and serve. They come out crunchy and delicious. For flavor variations, try adding soy sauce, chili powder, or garlic powder. This is perhaps the simplest use for whole seeds.

Hempseed Gomasio

4 ounces hulled hempseeds
1 teaspoon sea salt

Toast and grind the seeds, then blend them with the salt. Serve the gomasio over rice, salads, or steamed vegetables, or anywhere that you would use salt.

Hempwich Butter

1¼ cups hulled hempseeds
2 tablespoons hemp oil or olive oil
1 small clove garlic, pressed
1 teaspoon soy sauce
sea salt and pepper

Toast the seeds lightly (see 46). Once they have cooled, grind one cup of the seeds in a coffee grinder or blender. Combine the rest of the unground hulled seeds, the ground seeds, oil, and pressed garlic in a small bowl, and blend them thoroughly with a fork. Season with soy sauce, salt, and pepper. Add more oil for a softer consistency. Store the butter in a glass jar in the refrigerator. You'll find it tastes great on bagels or bread.

Note: Another way to produce nut butter is to grind toasted or untoasted hulled seeds in a Champion juicer using the blank attachment.

Puddings • Salad dressings •

Hemp Milk

2 cups hulled hempseeds
5 cups water
flavorings (vanilla, maple syrup, carob, or honey)

Grind the seeds into a paste. (Alternatively, don't grind the seeds, but steam them over water, then put them into the blender and proceed.) Heat the water and the ground seed paste in a pan, not letting it boil. Filter twice through cheesecloth and squeeze to get all the milk out. Add vanilla, maple syrup, carob powder, or honey and serve.

Source: Michael Holcomb

Hempseed Tahini

1 cup hulled hempseeds
1 tablespoon hemp oil
1 tablespoon water (optional)

Toast the seeds and finely grind them in a blender. Combine them with the oil and mix to a smooth paste. The mixture may require the water to keep it moist. Add the resulting tahini to homemade hempseed hummus (see below).

Hempseed Hummus

¾ cup hempseed tahini (see recipe above)
1 can (15 ounces) chickpeas
1 tablespoon hemp oil
½ cup lemon juice
3 to 4 cloves garlic
1 teaspoon soy sauce
freshly ground pepper
a pinch of cayenne pepper (optional)

Puree the chickpeas in a blender, add the other ingredients, and blend until the texture is smooth and creamy. Makes two cups.

Turkish Yogurt Sauce

1 cup yogurt
3 tablespoons hemp oil
1 clove garlic
salt and freshly ground pepper

Combine all the ingredients in a bowl and mix them together. Serve with spinach, kale, or cucumbers, or over rice. For a different flavor, add a few drops of soy sauce.

• *Salves* • *Sauces* • *Scones* •

Hempseed Veggie Rice Casserole

1 cup rice
2 cups water
1 cube vegetable bouillon or 1 tablespoon vegetable broth powder
1 tablespoon butter
1 medium onion
1 carrot
4 garlic cloves
2 tablespoons olive oil
1 small zucchini
2 eggs
1 teaspoon soy sauce
½ teaspoon salt
½ teaspoon pepper
1 teaspoon basil
½ cup water
½ cup hulled hempseeds
½ cup seasoned bread crumbs

Preheat the oven to 350° F (180° C). Place water, rice, vegetable bouillon cube or powder, and butter in a medium-size pot. Cover and heat until the mixture comes to a boil. Reduce the heat to medium and simmer for about 15 minutes. While the rice is cooking, dice the onion and carrot and mince the garlic. Saute the carrot, onion, and garlic in olive oil on medium heat for 3 minutes. While this mixture is cooking, dice and add the zucchini. Saute the mixture for 5 minutes more.

In a large bowl, scramble the eggs with soy sauce, salt, pepper, and basil. Stir in the water. Add the cooked rice, vegetables, seeds, and seasoned bread crumbs, and mix well. Place the mixture in an oiled baking dish, cover it, and bake it at 350° for 30 minutes. The casserole can be sliced when cool. Serves 5.

Source: Janet Crolius-Jacob

Hemp/Almond Pesto

½ cup toasted hulled hempseeds
⅔ cup sliced almonds
1 bunch basil
3 tablespoons hemp oil
3 tablespoons olive oil
2 cups grated parmesan cheese

Crush seeds, almonds, basil, hemp oil, and olive oil to a paste with a pestle in a mortar. Mix in the parmesan. Heat pesto in a pot, being careful not to cook it. Serve this tasty sauce over your favorite pasta. Sufficient for 1½ pounds of pasta. Finely cut tomato cubes add refreshing taste and color.

Source: Ralf Hiener: *Hanf: Das Kochbuch* (*Hemp: The Cookbook*).

Hadecke Verlag, Germany, 1998

Hemp-Oil Salad Dressing

3 tablespoons hemp oil
1 teaspoon balsamic vinegar
1 teaspoon fresh lemon juice
1 clove garlic
2- to 3-inch piece of fresh, peeled ginger
   (or less, according to taste)
sea salt
freshly ground pepper
finely chopped fresh herbs (chives, parsley, cilantro, etc.)

Press the ginger and garlic with a garlic press, combine the extracted liquids with all the other ingredients, and mix well. Add herbs, according to taste. Toss gently with salad, and perhaps sprinkle hulled hempseeds on top.

This dressing is as quick and easy to make as it is delicious. It goes with almost all green-leaf or vegetable salads, and is especially good with bitter salads such as arugula and dandelion, or mixed salads with tomatoes.

If you prepare multiple quantities, it will keep in the refrigerator for up to two weeks in a glass jar with a screw-top lid.

Smoothies • Snack chips • Sodas

Juicy Carrot Salad

8 large carrots
4 tablespoons hulled hempseeds
6 tablespoons hemp oil
2 tablespoon lemon juice
2- to 3-inch piece of fresh ginger (or less, according to taste)
sea salt

Grate the carrots coarsely. Toast the seeds lightly and add them to the grated carrots. Press the ginger in a garlic press and combine it with all the other ingredients. Pour the sauce over the carrots and seeds and toss well. Let the salad sit for at least half an hour before serving. Yields 4 servings.

Mediterranean Marinated Vegetables

3 red bell peppers
2 medium-size eggplants
3 small zucchinis
12 mushrooms
8 garlic cloves

For the marinade
2 twigs fresh rosemary
2 twigs fresh oregano
2 garlic cloves
12 tablespoons hemp oil
5 tablespoons (balsamic vinegar or lemon juice)
salt and freshly ground pepper

Cut bell pepper and mushrooms in quarters, cut eggplant and zucchini in finger- size slices. Spread on baking tray and broil for 15 minutes at 450° F (230° C), then turn and broil other side. Be careful not to burn the vegetables.

Meanwhile, mince herbs, press garlic cloves, and mix with all other marinade ingredients. Season with pepper and salt.

Arrange vegetables in casserole and cover the still-hot vegetables with the marinade. Let soak for at least six hours. Drain oil before serving cool as an appetizer; the drained oil can be used for salad dressing. The marinated vegetables keep well in the refrigerator for up to a week if no vinegar or lemon juice is added. Yields 6–8 servings.

Soaps • Sour cream • Spreads

Spinach Feta Quiche

Dough

2 cups wheat flour
1¼ cups hemp flour
1½ cups water
1 tablespoon salt

Filling

2 pounds fresh spinach
¼ cup toasted hempseeds
6 ounces feta cheese
½ cup yogurt or soy milk
1 onion
1 garlic clove
salt, pepper, nutmeg, basil

Combine all ingredients for dough in a bowl and knead thoroughly. Cover and let sit for 15 minutes, then knead again. Let sit for a few minutes, then roll out and put in well-greased round baking tin. Wash spinach leaves, drain well, and simmer in a pan with mashed garlic clove, chopped onion, and toasted seeds. Add yogurt or milk and spices and bring to a boil. Drain spinach well, spread it on the dough, and sprinkle with crumbled feta. Bake at 450° F (230° C) for 30-35 minutes, until feta is golden.

Hempseed Gravy

2 tablespoons butter or soy margarine
2 cups water
½ teaspoon salt
½ teaspoon pepper
1 teaspoon parsley
½ teaspoon garlic powder
3 tablespoons hulled hempseeds
1 tablespoon soy sauce
1 tablespoon Worcestershire sauce
1 tablespoon honey
3 tablespoons unbleached flour

Place all ingredients except the butter in a quart jar with a lid. Shake the jar vigorously until the flour is well mixed and no lumps remain. Melt the butter over medium heat in an iron frying pan or heavy pot. Pour the liquid into the pan and bring it to a slow boil. Stir the mixture well while it heats and let it simmer for 2 minutes. Makes about 2 cups.

Source: Janet Crolius-Jacob

• *Stir-fries* • *Tabouli* • *Tahini* •

Hemp Muffins

1¼ cups wheat flour
⅓ cup hemp flour
½ cup butter
2 large eggs
1 cup buttermilk
1 cup raw sugar
2 teaspoons baking powder
½ teaspoon salt
½ teaspoon powdered ginger
1½ teaspoons cinnamon

Beat melted butter, sugar, and salt in a bowl until frothy. Whisk eggs in a separate bowl and gradually combine with butter/sugar mixture. Mix wheat and hemp flours, spices, and baking powder in a separate bowl and alternately mix with small amounts of egg/butter mixture and buttermilk. Mix well. Put dough in greased muffin tin or paper cups and bake in preheated oven for 20 minutes at 400° F (200° C). Release from tin and sprinkle with cinnamon sugar or hulled hempseeds. Optional: substitute honey or stevia for part of the sugar.

Source: Ralf Buck: *Das Hanfbackbuch* (*The Hemp Baking Book*).
Verlag Die Werkstatt, Germany, 1998

Hemp Pancakes

1 cup Red Mill 10 Grain Stoneground
    or Arrowhead Pancake and Waffle Mix
½ cup toasted hulled hempseeds
1 egg (or ½ cup yogurt)
1 tablespoon hemp oil
1 cup water (or soy milk)

Grind seeds, blend with the mix, add egg or yogurt and oil, add water or milk for desired consistency, and cook. Top with your favorite topping or fill with your favorite filling.

Midnight Delight

½ cup hulled hempseeds
5 or 6 teaspoons maple syrup
¼ teaspoon vanilla

Put hulled seeds through a Champion juicer for the consistency of nut butter (see page 46), then mix together the rest of the ingredients; or alternatively, purchase nut butter and mix as directed. Form into tasty little balls or use as a dessert spread.   *Source:* Jan Wilson

Tapenade • Tempeh • Toffee • Tofu

Nutty Fruit Cake

1 cup sweet butter
1 to 1½ cups sugar
4 eggs
salt
2 teaspoons baking powder
1⅔ cups whole wheat flour
1¼ cups hemp flour
½ cup milk
1 cup raisins
1 cup candied ginger
1 cup dried fruit (cherries, blueberries, or apricots)
1 cup nuts (walnuts, hazelnuts, or pecan)
½ cup toasted hulled hempseeds

Slowly melt butter in pan and mix with sugar. Mix in eggs and milk and add salt. Combine wheat and hemp flours with baking powder and slowly add into butter/sugar/milk/egg mixture. Stir until smooth and mix in other ingredients. Spread in greased bread pan and bake at 350° F (180° C) for one hour.

Sweet Hemp Strips

1½ cups hulled hempseeds
½ cup honey

Lightly toast seeds in a pan, let cool, and finely grind 1 cup in coffee grinder (keep ½ cup for crust). Empty into midsize bowl. Add honey gradually and knead until smooth. Make sure mixture is solid enough and not too sticky. Roll out dough on a board or plate, ½ inch thick, and cut into 1 to 2-inch strips. Spread remaining unground seeds onto plate. Roll strips in seeds until completely covered. Store in refrigerator. This is an excellent example of the replacement of sesame seeds with hempseeds in traditional Mediterrean sweets.

T o r t i l l a s   •   T r a i l   m i x   •   T r u f f l e s

Sweet and Crunchy Hempseed Balls

2 cups dates, pitted and mashed
¼ cup hulled hempseed toasted
¼ cup hazelnuts or cashews or sunflower seeds
2 cups coconut flakes,
    or 1 cup raisins
½ cup oats
1 tablespoon honey
¼ cup sesame seed or hulled hempseeds

Toast hulled hempseeds in pan. Grind seeds and hazelnuts in coffee grinder. Mash and pit dates. Mix ground seeds, hazelnuts, dates coconut flakes, and oats and knead thoroughly, then mix in honey. Form small balls and roll in sesame seeds. Instead of sesame seeds, roll in coconut flakes, cracker crumbs, or coarsely ground nuts. Or substitute dates with dried figs.

Source: Hanfsamen und Hanföl. nova-Institute, Hürth, 1997

Hemp Cookies

½ cup butter
1 cup sugar
2 eggs
1 teaspoon vanilla
1¾ cups whole wheat flour
½ cup hemp flour or grounded toasted hulled hempseed
½ teaspoon baking soda
½ teaspoon salt
8 oz. chocolate chips
¾ cup walnuts
¼ cup hulled toasted hempseeds
½ teaspoon organic lemon peel
½ teaspoon lemon juice

Slowly melt butter in pan and add sugar. Add eggs and vanilla and beat until fluffy. Stir in flour, seeds and nuts, baking soda, and salt. Add other ingredients and mix well. Drop spoonfuls on greased cookie sheet. Bake at 375° F (190° C) for 12 minutes.

Source: The Hemp Seed Cook Book,
Carol Miller and Don Wirtshafter, Ohio Hempery, 1994

Veggie   burgers • Vinaigrette •

Try These Tips!

- In salads, use hemp oil as you would use olive, walnut, or pumpkinseed oil.

- For a quick salad dressing, mix miso and hemp butter with water, adding ginger for spice.

- Used hulled hempseeds in cakes, cookies, and trail mix.

- Use hulled hempseeds and hemp oil in dips and spreads.

- Sprinkle hulled hempseeds on homemade soups.

- Substitute up to ⅕ of wheat or rye flour in any recipe with hempseed flour.

- Try some seeds or a spoonful of hemp oil in your sauces.

- Sprinkle hulled hempseeds on breakfast cereals.

If you have your own hemp recipes and want to share them with others, email them to recipes@hemp-foods.com. *To discover new hemp recipes, visit* www.hemp-foods.com

Waffles • Whole grain bread

Glossary

Alpha-linolenic acid (18:3 omega-3)—A triple-unsaturated essential fatty acid, and an important precursor for a series of hormone-like substances, the prostaglandins. Symptoms of deficiency include general weakness, motoric problems, low metabolic rates, tingling sensations in limbs, tissue inflammation, edema, dry skin, and high blood pressure.

Amino acid—Basic building block of proteins. More than twenty amino acids are known, nine of which are essential. The body digests all proteins to amino acids and then rebuilds its own proteins

Cholesterol—A group of organic substances with vital functions. In cell membranes, cholesterol levels control stiffness or fluidity. Cholesterols are also precursors for steroid hormones and vitamin D. Major cholesterol sources in the diet include meats and dairy fats. Increased blood levels of the low-density lipoprotein (LDL) cholesterol, caused by excessive intake of saturated fats, smoking, and stress, are risk factors for atherosclerosis and cardiovascular diseases. Dietary treatment with linoleic acid and gamma-linolenic acid has been shown to rapidly decrease elevated blood-cholesterol levels.

Cis—A configuration of unsaturated fatty acids in which the two H-atoms next to a double bond occur on the same side of the fatty-acid chain. The double bond in the cis-form causes the fatty-acid chain to bend. Unsaturated fatty acids in plant-seed oils occur mostly in the cis-form.

Double bond—A reactive, thus unstable, linking between two carbon atoms in a molecule. A molecule containing at least one double bond is called unsaturated.

Essential amino acids—Any of the nine amino acids, which the human body cannot synthesize but must obtain through the diet. Hempseed protein contains all nine essential amino acids.

Essential fatty acids (EFAs)—Linoleic acid and alpha-linolenic acid are the two fatty acids that must be present in our diet. They are vital for normal body function, heart action, and tissue integrity. EFAs account for more than 75 percent of the fatty acids in hemp oil.

Fatty acid—The basic building unit of fats and oils and many other compounds, serving structural and energy-storage purposes. Most abundant in plant oils are the monounsaturated oleic acid, the polyunsaturated fatty acids linoleic and alpha-linolenic acid, and the saturated fatty acids stearic and palmitic acid. Saturated fatty acids contain only single, or saturated, bonds between C-atoms, making the molecules straight and stiff. Unsaturated fatty acids contain at least one bond, polyunsaturated fatty acids (PUFAs) at least two double bonds that cause the molecule to bend.

Flour—The material ground from seedmeal or seedcake, the residues of hempseeds after oil crushing. Varying with hulling and crushing technique, it contains largely protein, hulls, and residual oil, and is used for baking, brewing, or animal food.

Free radical—A molecule having unpaired electrons, usually short-lived and highly reactive. Initiates the oxidation of fatty acids.

Gamma-linolenic acid (GLA, 18:3 omega-6)—A triple-unsaturated fatty acid important in human metabolism. In healthy persons, it is synthesized from linoleic acid. If this process is impaired, supplementation with GLA may be successful in the treatment of atopic eczema, premenstrual syndrome, diabetic neuropathy, and arthritis.

Hemp—A generic name for coarse fibers from various natural plants. More specifically, hemp encompasses numerous varieties of the species *Cannabis sativa*. Unlike marijuana, industrial hemp varieties have been bred to maximize their fiber, seed, or oil yields. They contain only small amounts (0.05 to 1 percent) of THC, the psychoactive ingredient of marijuana.

Hulled hempseeds—After removal of the hulls, hempseeds contain about one-third protein, one-third fat, 10 percent carbohydrates, and virtually no THC, and are more versatile with respect to food uses than are whole hempseeds.

Linoleic acid (18:2 omega-6)—A double-unsaturated essential fatty acid in human nutrition; a precursor for gamma-linolenic acid and prostaglandins. In hemp oil, linoleic acid is the predominant fatty acid (50 to 70 percent of the total fatty acids).

Lipids—The general term for substances of a fatty nature, including fats and oils, waxes, phospholipids, lipoproteins, and cholesterol.

Marijuana—The flowers and leaves of those *Cannabis sativa* varieties that, unlike industrial hemp, contain significant concentrations (3 to 20 percent) of THC, the major psychoactive ingredient in Cannabis.

Meal—The seedmeal or seedcake is the residue after crushing the hempseeds for oil.

Omega (Ω or n)—The Greek letter used in the numbering system for fatty acids. Omega indicates the location of the first double bond from the hydrophobic methyl (nonacid) end of the fatty-acid chain. The omega-3 and omega-6 fatty-acid families have their first double bonds on the third and sixth carbon atom, respectively. Omega-3s and -6s are derived from the essential fatty acids alpha-linolenic and linoleic acid, respectively.

Parts per million (ppm) = milligram per kilogram (mg/kg)—A measurement for small concentrations of constituents or contaminants.

Phospholipids—Essential cell compounds, also present in plant oils, from which they are routinely removed during refining. The largest group of phospholipids are the lecithins. Unrefined hemp oil is a moderate source of phospholipids.

Prostaglandins—Substances derived from a fatty acid with hormone-like functions in the regulation of cell activity.

Protein—Any of large variable macromolecules built from up to several hundred amino acids, folded in specific three-dimensional shapes. Proteins act as enzymes, hormones, tissue components, and blood proteins.

Rancidification—The process of oxidative degradation of edible oil. It is promoted by light, heat, and oxygen and inhibited by antioxidants. Rancid oils are recognized by their buttery or painty flavor.

Saturated fatty acid—Contains only single, or saturated, bonds between C-atoms.

THC—The abbreviation for delta-9-tetrahydrocannabinol, the major psychoactive ingredient in marijuana.

Tocopherols—The chemical name for the relevant antioxidants in the vitamin E complex. Tocopherols serve as antioxidants both in the human body and in food.

Trans—The heat treatment and hardening (hydrogenation) of vegetable oils converts cis-double bonds in unsaturated fatty acids into the trans configuration. Both hydrogen atoms adjacent to the double bond occur on different sides, thus causing a straight fatty-acid chain.

Triglyceride—In foods, fatty acids occur primarily as triglycerides, which consist of three fatty acids of varying chain lengths and degree of unsaturation, attached with ester bonds to a glycerol backbone.

Unsaturated fatty acids—Contains at least one double bond.

Vitamin E—The generic name for a group of essential nutrients, including tocopherols. The biological function of vitamin E is based on its strong antioxidant properties; it slows the oxidative breakdown of structural lipids in membranes caused by free-radical attack. Vitamin E is also a natural antioxidant in plant oils.

Bibliography

The following is a only a partial list of references to the topics covered in this book. Its intent is to provide the reader access to more detailed books and articles.

1 Bócsa, Iván and Michael Karus: *The Cultivation of Hemp: Botany, Varieties, Cultivation and Harvesting.* HEMPTECH, Sebastopol, CA, 1998.

2 Cunnane, Stephen C. and Lilian U. Thompson (Eds.): *Flaxseed in Human Nutrition.* AOCS Press, Champaign, IL, 1995.

3 Deferne, Jean-Luc and David W. Pate: Hempseed oil: a source of valuable essential fatty acids. *Journal of the International Hemp Association*, 3 (1):1-7, 1996.

4 Editorial: Tocotrienols may protect against breast cancer / Vitamin E, antioxidants prevent brain cell death. *INFORM*, 9 (11):1066-1067, 1998.

5 Erasmus, Udo: *Fats That Heal, Fats That Kill.* Alive Books, Vancouver, B.C., Canada, 1994.

6 Haumann, Barbara F.: Alternative sources for n-3 fatty acids / Complex issue: ALA's conversion to long chain n-3. *INFORM*, 9 (12):1108-1118, 1998.

7 Huang, Yung-Sheng and David E. Mills: *Gamma-Linolenic Acid: Metabolism and Its roles in Nutrition and Medicine.* AOCS Press, Champaign, IL, 1995.

8 Idson, B.: Dry skin: moisturizing and emolliency. *Cosmetics and Toiletries*, 107 (7):69-78, 1992.

9 Jones, Kenneth: *Nutritional and Medicinal Guide to Hemp Seed.* Rainforest Botanical Laboratory, Gibsons, B.C., Canada, 1995.

10 Kruger, M. C. and D. F. Horrobin: Calcium metabolism, osteoporosis, and essential fatty acids: a review. *Progress in Lipid Research*, 36 (2-3):131-151, 1997.

11 Miller, Carol and Don Wirtshafter: *The Hemp Seed Cookbook.* The Ohio Hempery, OH, 1994

12 Mölleken, H. and Husmann, H.: Cannabinoids in seed extracts of Cannabis sativa cultivars. *Journal of the International Hemp Association*, 4 (2):73-79, 1997.

13 Mölleken, Helga and Theimer, Roland R.: Survey of minor fatty acids in Cannabis sativa L. fruits of various origins. *Journal of the International Hemp Association*, 4 (1):13-17, 1997.

14 nova-Institute (Ed.): Hanfsamen und Hanföl als Lebens- und Heilmittel. Verlag die Werkstatt, Germany, 1998.

15 nova-Institute (Ed.): THC limits for food. HEMPTECH, Sebastopol, CA, 1998.

16 West, Dave: Industrial hemp farming: history and practice. 1998. Available at www.pressenter.com/~davewest/IndHmpFrmg.htm

17 West, Dave: Hemp and marijuana: myths and realities. Prepared for the North American Industrial Hemp Council (NAIHC), 1998. Available at www.naihc.org.

18 Zambiazi, Rui C. and Roman Przybylski: Effect of endogenous minor components on the oxidative stability of vegetable oils. Lipid Technology, (5): 58-62, May 1998.

Additional Reading

Michael Bockisch: *Fats and Oils Handbook.* AOCS Press, Champaign, IL, 1998.

A comprehensive and detailed reference to technical and nutritional aspects of oils and fats.

INFORM (*International News on Fats, Oils and Related Materials*)

Published monthly by the AOCS Press for the American Oil Chemists' Society. An excellent and current review of technical, nutritional and market aspects for the food oil industry.

John Roulac: *Hemp Horizons: The Comeback of the World's Most Promising Plant.* Chelsea Green, White River Junction, VT, 1997.

An overview of the status and challenges of the hemp industry worldwide.

John Roulac: *Industrial Hemp.* HEMPTECH, Sebastopol, CA, 1995.

A brief introduction to the farming, processing, and uses of hemp.

nova-Institute (Ed.): *Bioresource Hemp.* Proceedings of the two symposia held in Frankfurt, Germany in 1995 and 1997. Distributed in the United States by HEMPTECH, Sebastopol, CA.

These two volumes are excellent compilations of relevant scientific and applied research on all aspects related to industrial hemp.

See www.hemptech.com for further hemp literature.

About the Authors

GERO LESON has worked for more than fifteen years as an environmental scientist and consultant to industry, both in his native Germany and in the United States. He has helped implement several innovative environmental technologies and concepts, including industrial crops such as hemp. His goal is to expand the use of such crops by supporting the implementation of appealing product lines such as hempseeds and hemp oil. With the German nova-Institute, he has organized several international symposia on industrial hemp. Gero holds a Masters degree in Physics from the University of Cologne, Germany, and a doctorate in Environmental Science and Engineering from UCLA. He is the principal of Leson Environmental Consulting in Berkeley, California.

PETRA PLESS has worked as an environmental consultant for the past eight years, in both Germany and the U.S., and is an associate with Leson Environmental Consulting. Petra has published her research on several ecological and environmental issues. She holds a Masters degree in Biology from the Technical University of Munich, Germany, and is completing a doctorate in Environmental Science and Engineering at UCLA. Her dissertation explores the environmental aspects of hemp farming and the manufacture of hemp products, in a life-cycle assessment.

JOHN W. ROULAC is the author of *Industrial Hemp, Hemp Horizons,* and the best-seller *Backyard Composting.* He is the founder and president of HEMPTECH, The Industrial Hemp Information Network; the founder of HEMPBROKERS.com, a hempseed-product supplier; and the founder and president of Harmonious Technologies, America's leading home-composting firm. John serves as board secretary on the North American Industrial Hemp Council. He has spoken on more than a hundred radio programs, and is frequently quoted in publications ranging from the *Wall Street Journal* to *Wired* magazine.

ORDER FORM

If your favorite retailer or catalog is sold out of *Hemp Foods and Oil for Health,*
please use this order form.

✳ **Fax orders:** (419) 281-6883

☎ **Telephone orders:** Call toll-free 24 hours: (800) 265-4367
or call (419) 281-1802
M/C and Visa accepted.

✉ **Postal orders:** Make check payable to Bookmasters,
1444 U.S. Route 42, Ashland, OH 44805   USA

? **Inquiries:** Call (707) 823-2800, email orders@hemptech.com, or visit
www.hemptech.com

Retail Price $6.95. Volume discounts available.

Sales tax
Please add 7.25% for books shipped to California addresses.

Shipping & handling
$2 per book U.S., $3 Canada and Mexico, $4 all others

Payment
❏ Check   ❏ Visa   ❏ Mastercard   ❏ American Express

Card number _____

Name on card _____ Expiration date _____

Number of books ordered _____   Amount enclosed _____

Company Name _____

Name and Title _____

Address _____

City _____ State _____ Zip _____

Telephone (_____) _____

Email _____

Also available through HEMPTECH:
Hemp Horizons: The Comeback of the World's Most Promising Plant,
The Cultivation of Hemp: Botany, Varieties, Cultivation and Harvesting,
Industrial Hemp: Practical Products—Paper to Fabric to Cosmetics, and a range of books,
reports, and videos.